When we embrace all of our sexuality, we honor our spirituality.

When we embrace all of our spirituality, we honor our sexuality.

When we embrace both, we celebrate God.

Sacred Orgasms
Kenneth Ray Stubbs

The Massage Team

Standing L to R: Cliff Berrien, Tim Dingman, Tim Townsend-Kuhns, Jacob Palafox,
John E. Kent III, Delbert Pentz-Newsome
Lower L to R: Joseph Kramer, Kenneth Ray Stubbs, Jim Dennis

MALE

erotic massage

A Guide to Sex and Spirit

author

Kenneth Ray Stubbs, Ph.D.

photographer

Jim Dennis

Secret Garden Publishing
Tucson, AZ

Published by
Secret Garden Publishing
5631 W. Placita del Risco
Dept. M
Tucson, Arizona 85745

Photography: Jim Dennis
Cover Photo: Jim Dennis
Author's Photo: Jim Dennis
Photographer's Photo: Robert Sequeri
James Broughton's Photo: Joel Singer
Cover and Book Design: Richard Stodart

ISBN 0-939263-16-5

RECOMMENDATION

LAY THE BOOK FLAT
TO LEARN
THE STROKES

1. Take *Male Erotic Massage* to a "fast print" shop.
2. For a few dollars, have the shop
   a. cut off the binding,
   b. punch comb-binding holes near the binding edge,
   c. and place a comb binding on the edge.

A Word of Caution

The purpose of this book is to educate. It is not intended to give medical or psychological therapy. Whenever there is concern about physical or emotional illness, a qualified health professional should be consulted, especially when the illness is long-term or potentially terminal.

The authors, photographers, and the publisher shall have neither liability nor responsibility to any person or entity with respect to any loss, damage, injury, or ailment caused or alleged to be caused directly or indirectly by the information or lack of information in this book.

DEDICATED TO

James Broughton

He sings his songs
and I dance

Contents

James Broughton

Song of the Godbody

James Broughton

This is my body which speaks for itself
This is my body which speaks for all men
This is my body which sings of itself
This is the song of the Godbody

I breathe you I contain you I propel you
I am your opening and closing
I am your rising and falling
I am your thrust and surrender

I stiffen you I melt you I energize
I quicken your humor and heartache
I set the spark to your fluid
I stir your mixable blessing

I am your inside operator
I stretch I sweat I maneuver
I flex your will and your man power
I polish your launching pad

I prime your engines of quest
I fan your spontaneous combustion
I drive your vehicle of dreams
I accelerate your valor and risk

I am at the root of your folly
I am at the top of your form
In you I caper and flourish
In you I become what I am

You are my cheerful vicissitude
You are my sturdy weakness
I am your faithful bedfellow
I am your tenacious secret

I connect your links
I replenish your seeds
I bathe in your bloodstream
I bask in the raw of your nature

I am the conductor of pulse and impulse
I am the director of anatomical play
You are my theater of nervous charades
You are my circus of knack and bungle

I am your unheeded prompter
I am the slips of your tongue
I am the catch in whatever you think
I am the quirk in what you are sure of

I carry a lantern through your labyrinth
I call to you from your vitals
You hear me best when you marvel
You hear me least when you whimper

You are my ancient you are my child
You are the brother of all your heroes
My earnest monkey My ticklish lion
You are my zoo and my sanctum

I tune up your instruments
I play on your organs
I strum in your breast
I croon in your head

I elixirate your phallus
I enter your every orifice
I impregnate every beginning
I effervesce I rhapsodize

You plunge into motley waters
You catch on fire when you love
You are my liquid opal
You are my burning bush

I sprout your sperm and your egg
I spawn the engodments of flesh
I shape the new body of Adam
I reshape the old body of Eve

I engender all the women of men
I generate the men of all women
I love you in every man's body
I live you in every man's lover

Trust that I know my own business
Cherish your fact and your fettle
Respect your perpetual motion
Relish your frisky divinity

You are my ripening godling
You are my fidgety angel
You are my immortal shenanigan
You are my eroding monument

I am ever your lifelong bodyguard
I am always your marathon dancer
Let your feet itch with my glory
Dance all the way to your death

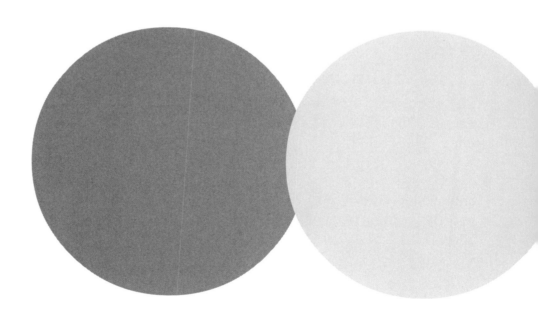

Foreword

Jack Morin, Ph.D.

Jack Morin is a psychotherapist and sex therapist in private practice in San Francisco. He is the author of The Erotic Mind, *a bold new psychology of desire and arousal, and was the recent president of the Western Region of the Society for the Scientific Study of Sexuality.*

When his doctoral dissertation evolved into his first book, Anal Pleasure and Health, *he made a major contribution to the deeper understanding of the body and sexuality. His compassionate confrontation with one of our most taboo topics is a model for us all. I hold him in the highest esteem.*

K.R.S.

The more we learn about mind-body development, the more obvious the elemental power of touch becomes. Infants left untouched wither, withdraw into isolation, and sometimes die. Without adequate sensual stimulation, the natural burst of brain growth during the first few years of life slows to a crawl. For adults, the importance of touch shifts from mere survival to the quality of our lives and loves. And how could it be otherwise? After all, wanted touch has awesome potentials to soothe, to nurture, to arouse, to foster connection, to heal, to uplift, and to enlighten.

We humans are innately touch-seekers and touch-givers. Of course, how we go about satisfying or avoiding our needs for touch varies tremendously. All too often the beckoning urge for skin-to-skin contact is inhibited by cultural and family prohibitions against the perceived dangers of sensual and sexual curiosity. As a result, many of us experience pleasure-anxiety, an uneasy feeling when touch becomes too intimate, too expansive, too moving, or too deeply exciting.

Ray Stubbs's work is a clarion call to all of us who seek to recognize and release our inhibitions and open ourselves to the power and meaning of intentional, conscious touch. His approach to erotic massage is deceptively simple, and yet it offers numerous doorways to self-discovery.

I'm particularly pleased that Ray has designed this new book for all men, but especially for gay and bi men. The fact that gays have been rejected from the dominant culture continues to have paradoxical effects. On the one hand, our view from the outside has helped to make us sexual pioneers and explorers. Since we can take so little for granted, we tend to be more conscious about sexual matters.

At the same time, internalized homophobia takes an enormous toll. Even those of us who openly celebrate gayness may still feel deeply wounded and ambivalent about our eroticism. Sexual conflicts that permeate the entire society may be even more pronounced among gays. For many, sex exists in a separate corner of life, cut off from its more "respectable" aspects. As a sex therapist, I regularly meet gay and bi men who are masters of pure, disconnected lust, but who suddenly feel awkward and frightened—and turned off—when they try to express their lust in the context of emotional closeness. Similarly, gay sex, especially of the casual variety, tends to be genitally focused, often to the exclusion of the rest of the body.

Straight or mostly-straight men who are drawn to intimate touch with other guys typically fear that others (or themselves) might consider them gay after all, although this is by no means necessarily the case. Conscious touch between men, with or without an erotic dimension, offers the palpable possibility of healing the aching chasm that separates man from man. This alienation often leads to violence and despair. Another inhibiting force for straight guys, just as for gays, is the tendency to focus on the allure of genital arousal, and thus to lose sight of so many other sensuous options.

Erotic massage offers us endless opportunities to discover the entire body as a vast erogenous zone. And as the body becomes eroticized, we're more inclined to experience sexuality as thoroughly woven into the tapestry of our lives. When I was studying peak erotic experiences for my book, *The Erotic Mind*, I was constantly struck by the multitude of ways that our favorite turn-ons link us with the challenges, hurts, joys, and deep meanings of our lives. Eros includes sex, but is so much larger and richly complex. No wonder erotic massage can trigger unexpected emotions, vivid images, and curiously different sensations. Understandably, we may feel a bit overwhelmed at times. But when we remain present, in spite of an urge to shut down, we are richly rewarded.

For givers and receivers alike, erotic massage is a pathway to an expanded sense of self. During highly pleasurable moments, the distinction between giver and receiver vanishes. To receive touch unselfconsciously from another is to give it back, only amplified. Likewise, touch generously given is at least as much a gift to oneself as it is to the other. When touch flows so seamlessly, we may simultaneously transcend other perceived opposites, including the pervasive splits between mind/body, sex/spirit, top/bottom, and masculine/feminine.

None of these possibilities is as esoteric as it may sound. Part of the beauty of Ray's approach is that it can be enjoyed at all levels of skill. Beginners needn't worry about doing it "wrong." There is no grading system for erotic massage, only degrees of enjoyment. At the same time, with practice, patience, and a playful attitude, we naturally become more skillful giver-receivers, and more fluent in the language of touch.

Explorers of full-body, erotic touch may need to move past a tricky hurdle. During extended sessions, our hard-ons will probably come and go as arousal naturally waxes and wanes. For those steeped in the rigors of hard-or-forget-it sex, changeable erections may be quite disconcerting or even frightening. But for those who are willing to hang in there, hard or not, I can think of no better way for a man to improve his sex life than to liberate his eroticism from the tyranny of erectile expectations. This is one reason why erotic massage can be so beneficial for those who are worried about their sexual functioning; it is a powerful antidote to performance anxiety.

Erotic massage is also a wonderful gift that long-term partners can give to each other, even after old passions have cooled considerably. Ray's approach offers ways to be sensuous and erotic that transcend the widespread, yet destructive belief that erotic pleasure must be fueled by burning passion. Many massages that start out warmly end up generating unexpected heat—but not always, of course. For committed companions who are more comfortable than passionate, I'm an advocate of "warm sex." Because it is so flexible and different from our typical sexual routines, erotic massage can provide a new framework for releasing us from burdensome expectations that only set us up for disappointment.

I've heard more than a few of my male clients refer to erotic massage as "Bambi sex" or "hopelessly vanilla," usually before they've let themselves fully explore it. Not only does Ray's approach embrace our intriguing kinks and quirks—where would we be without them?—but it invites us on a journey as adventurous and compelling as even the most elaborate sex scene can ever be. Oil, anyone?

Introduction to Erotic Massage

Joseph Kramer, M.Div.

Joseph Kramer is a friend, colleague, and fellow pioneer bringing sex and spirit into the light. For almost two decades throughout Europe and North America, we followed similar paths teaching massage that embraces sexuality. Holding a Master of Divinity degree, Joseph is the founder of EROSpirit Research Institute in Oakland, California, where he now produces a variety of videos on sexuality.

I am honored Joseph is willing to introduce this book by writing of his evolution into a world barely realized in cultures where men touching men tenderly is a taboo, where sex is basically still a sin.

K.R.S.

I am a masseur and teacher of massage. Although I have given hundreds of wonderful massages to women, my specialty is touching men. In fact, in the last twenty years I have massaged more than 10,000 men. I am honored to say that laying hands on men is the "great work" of my life. I would like to share with you some of the wisdom that has come to me giving, receiving, and teaching massage.

In 1979, as I was completing my master's degree at the Graduate Theological Union in Berkeley, I realized that for too long I had been studying literature, psychology, mathematics, and philosophy, but that I had had no formal education in the subject that intrigued me most—pleasuring a man. My traditional quest for knowledge had taken me deep into the realm of words and ideas. Yet, I had forgotten the wisdom available to me within my own body and within the bodies of those around me. I trusted a voice within me that said, "Look for a teacher." Two weeks later I was enrolled in the Berkeley School of Massage in their professional certification program. I found it humorous that many of my class-conscious friends were horrified that I was training to become a manual laborer. But that hundred-hour massage training has had more impact on my life than all the thousands of class hours I endured during my undergraduate and graduate education.

I had had one full-body massage just as I began graduate school. John Coleman, my academic advisor in Berkeley, announced to a group of students that he had just completed a course in Esalen Massage and he was looking for bodies to practice on. I volunteered. Although I knew this massage would not be erotic, I feared I might get an erection since I was to be naked. Before he began the massage, John explained the goal of Esalen massage was to awaken consciousness throughout my body. "The long, slow strokes from your head to your feet and back again are to give you a sense of wholeness and well-being." It was interesting that this massage was not about tense muscles. I was surprised that I had nothing to do but breathe and enjoy and surrender.

There were parts of me that woke up during that massage that had been asleep for years. My whole body screamed yes to this touch experience. Yes! Yes! Yes! This massage was, without a doubt, the most significant two hours of my first twenty-five years. An older man had initiated me into a new way of feeling and being a body. That massage helped me discover my vocation, my life path.

All men need to be touched. There is no place in America that suffers more from the legacy of rugged individualism than the male body. As boys enter their teen years, they are overtly and covertly initiated into the loneliness and isolation of being a man. The mantra of my childhood, chanted nonstop by teachers and parents, was "Keep your hands to yourself." I am sad to say I heeded the adults' warnings. As a teenager, I was consumed by skin hunger that I felt only as generalized rage. I totally identified with Paul Simon's lyrics, "I touch no one and no one touches me. I am a rock. I am an island." In my early twenties, I was Tommy, the boy who plaintively reached out his arms, singing, "See me, feel me, touch me, heal me." I still hear those words thirty years later in the men I touch on a daily basis.

A San Francisco masseur once wrote that after giving a thousand massages, the masseur becomes enlightened. I am not sure what "enlightened" means, but I do know that I have become extremely sensitive to my clients. I have educated my empathic skills so that, if I choose to, I can feel in my body what the man I am massaging is feeling. This helps me focus on tensions and places where he might be feeling pain.

Many times, after I had finished what I thought was an excellent session, I would feel a deep dissatisfaction in the man I had just massaged. Although I had been sensuous and intimate with most of his body, I had chosen not to touch his genitals. This is the norm in massage therapy today. But, instead of the man feeling his body being massaged into wholeness, he feels a split between the parts that I touched and the parts I didn't touch. This dilemma has always been with bodyworkers and other touch therapists.

In 1983 I transgressed professional boundaries and became an erotic masseur. As AIDS began to spread among men who had sex with other men, I recognized a need for a new, no-risk erotic way of connecting and playing. And so I developed and taught Taoist Erotic Massage. This astonishing combination of conscious breathing and genital stimulation activates highly pleasurable states within a man's body without having ejaculation as the goal. Erotic massage is a wonderful intimacy for one man to offer another.

In 1984, I founded the Body Electric School of Massage in Oakland, California, after reading the research of the brilliant developmental neuro-psychologist James Prescott. According to Prescott's studies, "deprivation of physical affection in human relationships . . . constitutes the single greatest source of physical violence in human societies."[1] Prescott's studies of dozens of cultures convinced me that massage was an important antidote to violence. In other words, to know how to pleasure a man's body is to know how to stop violence in today's world. This essential truth of men's liberation was missed by the leaders of the so-called "men's movement." In fact, Iron John not only never gives or receives a massage, for all we know, he doesn't have a penis.

Massage separates the acts of giving and receiving. Many men discover that they are very good at giving massage but terrible when it comes to receiving. They can't let go of being in control. They don't trust themselves or the masseur enough just to receive. I have learned to let go into the pleasure of receiving touch by focusing on the effortless exhaling of each breath. And I have helped many men who were having trouble with receiving pleasure by guiding them in conscious breathing where all of their effort is on the inhale and the exhale leaves their lungs like a gentle breeze.

I have also massaged hundreds of men who have had life-threatening illnesses. When I touch men who are close to death, I try to let go of my own sense of time. This moment is all there is. I emphasize energy work like acupressure on those men who are sick or close to death, because often men who are dying do not want to be grounded in the body they are preparing to leave.

After giving thousands of massages, I realize that I continue to touch men because of the mystery I feel in the act of touching. In other words, touching men is my spiritual path and my meditation practice. Touching men is where I contact the sacredness of life.

This book you hold in your hands about men massaging men is not for your coffee table. This is a guidebook for your hands and your heart. A guidebook to a powerful spiritual path.

Touch me. Touch the palm of your hand to my body as I pass. Be not afraid of my body.

As Adam Early in the Morning
Walt Whitman

[1] "Phylogenetic and Ontogenetic Aspects of Human Affectional Development" by James W. Prescott in *Progress in Sexology: Selected Papers from the Proceedings of the 1976 International Congress of Sexology*, ed. by Robert Gemme and Connie Christine Wheeler, Plenum Press, 1977, p. 449. Also see "Body Pleasure and the Origins of Violence," James W. Prescott, *The Futurist*, April 1975.

THE MASSAGE STROKES

Kenneth Ray Stubbs, Ph.D.

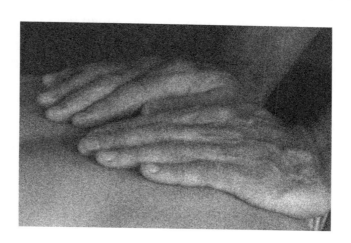

THE JOURNEY

Learning massage is a journey to the soul.

Consciously touching another, whether he be friend, family, lover, or stranger, is a dance with the soul of another.

Yes, we stroke the physical. Yet, the touch goes deeper. We nurture the Godbody. Our hands become the expression of our heart touching flesh embracing heart.

The techniques that follow in this book can bring us to an experience of these words.

To come to such a place, where we are at one with another, his physical body and his Godbody, may take many hours of exploration, of practice, of giving and receiving massage.

At first, learning massage techniques will most likely feel awkward. Stay with your focus, and over time the parts can become a whole.

Remember these techniques are but a few of a myriad of possible strokes and styles of massage. Always be open to your own creativity. Adapt, modify, develop your own expression. This is what the first human doing massage had to do.

During a massage, either or both of you might feel erotic. You might or might not engage in any of a variety of sexual expressions before, during, or after a massage. However, should sex or orgasm become the sole goal, you might miss many other pleasures.

Sleep may occur. Laughter or tears or other feelings and memories are always possibilities. The body is alive. It has memory. And our touch can awaken both the agony and the ecstasy. It is all natural.

Allow each moment and each feeling to unfold itself. Many inner beauties can be discovered.

Let the massage be the meditation. The essentials of the journey are touch, presence, and compassion.

Trust, joy, and pleasure are the gift given and received.

PREPARATIONS

Many ingredients go into a massage. Some are more essential than others, depending on the situation, the focus, and the time available. Adaptation and innovation are often the key.

Here are the basics you will need.

- A willing recipient.

   A friend may or may not be interested in receiving a massage at a given moment. We can only offer an invitation. If the response is no, be open to connecting in other ways.

- A quiet place without interruptions.

   Ask housemates to refrain from excessive volumes. Turn off the phone ringer. Maybe put a "Do not disturb" sign on the door.

- A warm place.

   Since the recipient is usually physically inactive during the massage and the skin will be oiled, he will usually need warmer temperatures. A space heater may be necessary. Of course, if you are on a tropical beach . . .

- Oil.

   The following strokes assume oil is the medium. If this is unacceptable or unavailable, a powder such as cornstarch is a possibility for some of the strokes.

   Coconut oil from a natural food store is personally my first choice for an unscented vegetable oil (though coconut oil solidifies in even cool temperatures and may have to be heated for easy use).

   Many commercially prepared massage oils or lotions are now available in boutiques and natural food stores. Make sure any added fragrance is not excessive and will be a desirable addition.

   Baby oil is simply mineral oil with fragrance added. Moreover, there is controversy over the healthfulness of long-term use of mineral oil.

   Lotions are usually very sensual, but because they are partly water, they usually dry too quickly for a massage.

The oil is usually more accessible when in a squeeze bottle or a bottle with a push pump. If a bowl is your only possibility, be careful not to knock it over.

- The massage surface.

     All the massage strokes here are based on using a massage table. I have often adapted the techniques to beds, kitchen tables with a foam pad added, a carpeted floor covered by a sheet, or a large towel out in nature.

     Without a massage table, however, you might find yourself tiring quickly or feeling a strain in the back. If you as the giver find the massage laborious, the receiver is likely to sense this and not relax as deeply. As a valid option, you might massage only a few sections, such as the back and neck or just the feet.

     Basically, if a massage is not enjoyable to all involved, maybe dance another way, such as going on a picnic or to the symphony.

- A sheet and a towel.

     For the massage surface, choose a sheet that is okay to be oiled. You may or may not be able to wash out the oil spots. Also, an often-used sheet can develop a rancid oil smell.

     Rarely does massage oil soak in enough for the recipient to feel comfortable putting on clothing without wiping first. One or more towels will be necessary.

     Especially in colder temperatures, more than one towel or maybe a blanket might be preferable to cover parts not currently being massaged.

- Supportive cushions.

     A covered foam pad or a couple of rolled towels placed under the recipient's ankles when he is lying front down can prevent uncomfortable pressure on the front of the feet.

     The same padding under the recipient's knees when he is lying on his back might eliminate strain in his lower back while in that position.

- Music.

     Music can enhance the massage.

     Dominating rhythms, though, can interfere with the naturally changing rhythm in a massage. And almost any lyrics can keep the recipient's attention in the mental rather than the sensory realms.

Personally, I have found most classical music to be unsuitable, whereas music labeled as meditative or the like has helped deepen the massage experience, sometimes profoundly.

Much experimentation may be necessary for you to find what suits you best.

- Interior design.

    The general ambiance of the massage location can add a sensual delight when your friend first enters the space. Flowers, very mild incense, candlelight or colored light, soft music, and more are possibilities.

    Ultimately, though, your hands will be the most important factor.

- Sensual accessories.

    If available, before you apply any oil, maybe stroke feathers, furry mitts, or silky cloth across your friend. Experiment with other textures.

    Again, ultimately your hands will be the most important accessory.

GUIDELINES

In the massage style that follows, three basics are prominent.

- First, be present.

    Expectations and comparisons only interfere. Simply, be here now.

- Second, maintain full-hand contact when possible.

    In this massage style, allow your palms, fingers, and thumbs to contour the varied mountains and valleys of your friend's physical body. Always there are exceptions.

- Third, blend your movements into a continuous flow.

    Initially, we learn individual techniques. Eventually, we find the art of massage is a graceful stream becoming the next moment.

Remember also that far more important than the techniques is the connection between your friend and you. Initially, one is giver and one is receiver. Then when the strokes become an integrated flow, the give-receive duality disappears. And we become the dance of one.

Here are a few more suggestions to keep in mind.

- Nudity is never essential but usually better.

    Especially with the massage style that follows, full nudity is far more intimate. Yet, if either or both prefer for any reason to remain partially clothed, this is always to be respected. Pleasure flows more fully and easily where one's personal choices are supported.

- Touch your own inner peace before beginning a massage.

    We can slow our breath or use other meditation methods.

- Go by the body, not by the book.

    If our friend enjoys our massage, we are doing the strokes correctly. "Feels good" is the criteria regardless of written text.

- Vary the pressure, the tempo, and the rhythm.

    Repeating a stroke in exactly the same way each time may become boring.

- When in doubt, lighter pressure might be better.

    Ask occasionally if you are uncertain, especially when first learning massage. A nurturing, sensual focus rather than an athletic emphasis is central in the strokes that follow. However, your friend might actually prefer firmer pressure.

- Vary the sequence of strokes if preferable.

    The arrangement of strokes that follows is excellent for me, perhaps not for you.

- When there are two, massage both.

    Excluding the left arm, for example, after stroking the right can be very disconcerting for the receiver. Though massaging just the head, or just both feet, or just the front of both legs is usually fine.

- Glide on and off.

    Rather than initiating a touch with a sudden contact, glide on with a slow descent in the direction your hands will be stroking. (In a laying-on-of-hands "stroke," we simply allow our hands to slowly descend straight down.) When you are ready for your hands to leave the body, continue the stroke in a gradual ascent.

- Minimize the landings and takeoffs.

    Somewhere a perspective developed that the giver should never discontinue physical contact until the end of a massage. Nice in theory, such a practice unfortunately often results in distracting or uncomfortable touch. Massaging on the floor, for example, could be very stressful or painful without discontinuing contact as you move around.

- Minimize the verbal.

    Talking can extremely limit the awareness of sensory pleasures. Yet, should strong emotions, positive or negative, come up during the massage, allow space for that to unfold as well.

- Massage the whole body or only a part.

    Time limitations, location, temperature, passion, and personal preferences can all be factors in this choice.

- Prepare your hands.

    Unless they are very smooth, watches and jewelry are best removed. Fingernails also need to be smooth. In general, the longer your fingernails, the more modifications you will need to make. And be certain your hands are warm.

- Ask the recipient his preferences.

    Preferred strokes and places vary from person to person, from one time to the next. Remember, give only what you feel comfortable giving. Never force yourself.

    Also, even though genital massage strokes are in this book, allow them to be an option consensually chosen.

- Invite the recipient to relax.

  > Once everything is ready and your friend is lying down, invite him to take a few fuller, slower breaths, to close his eyes, and to sink into the padding beneath.

- Refinement of doing massage comes with both giving and receiving massage.

  > Be certain to arrange to be on the receiving end from time to time.

- Health and safer-sex are very important to us all. See the next section.

Massage is an art. And each massage is a unique experience.

Like Michelangelo, smooth away the rough edges so the beauty beneath can reveal itself.

HEALTH AND SAFER-SEX

When we massage, we share intimacy. Health is an essential question here, especially when we are or are about to be erotic with another. Without open and honest communication, nagging thoughts in the back of our minds can greatly limit the communion.

Be open to sharing information and any concerns with your friend before giving a massage. The suggestions below are some guidelines. The final choices are your and your friend's responsibility.

- If in doubt, consult a health professional. This book cannot anticipate all situations.

- With colds and flus, we can choose how close we want to be. A massage would often, though not always, feel better later.

- Forgo contact with any infectious area of the skin. Perhaps keep it clothed.

- Ask your friend if he has any tender areas. Perhaps exclude such an area, or at least be especially gentle there. With severe injuries and circulation problems, consult a health professional.

- The recipient may need to remove his contact lenses if you plan to massage his eyes.

- Generally, massage is considered a no-risk or very-low-risk safer-sex activity. Available at pharmacies, latex or vinyl examination gloves can provide additional barrier protection should either giver or receiver prefer for all or parts of the massage.

- A condom with a few drops of water-based lubricant placed in the tip and then rolled on the penis is another form of barrier protection. You would need to modify the following strokes some, but the sensations can still be exquisite.

    Remember that the vegetable or mineral oil you are using for the massage can deteriorate the latex of a condom, and thus render it useless for some other forms of erotic play.

For friends in acute states of illness, massage may not be the best way to express our love. Hugging, holding hands, and gentle caresses on the face are among other ways to say we care. Here, be sensitive, be appropriate, be compassionate.

BEGINNING

Friend's Position: Lying front down with arms by side.
Your Position: Initially at your friend's left side.

1 Centering

Your hands can be by your side (as in the image), in a prayer position in front of your heart, or as you prefer.
Your hands could be oiled before beginning unless you prefer to use feathers or furry mittens after the initial touch in the next step.

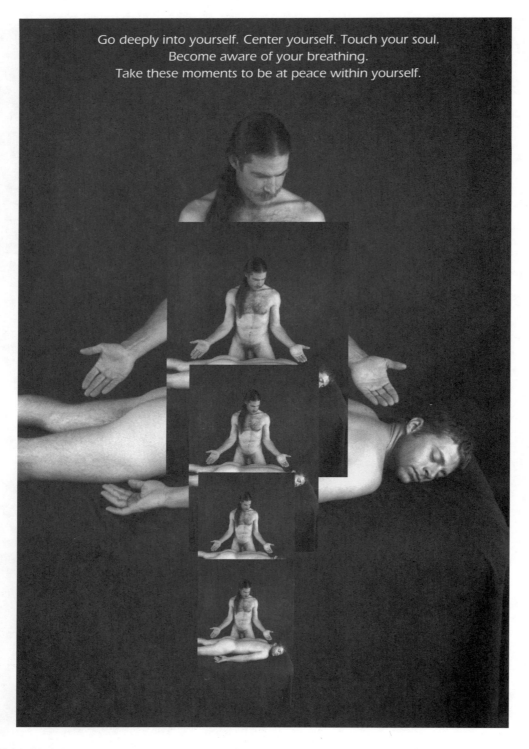

Go deeply into yourself. Center yourself. Touch your soul.
Become aware of your breathing.
Take these moments to be at peace within yourself.

2·A

Now bring your awareness to your friend
    resting quietly before you.
Slowly lower your palms. Perhaps you will feel
    warmth or subtle vibrations several
    inches above your friend's back.
Here, take a moment to silently honor your
    friend. In a sense, you are nonverbally
    asking permission to touch both his
    Godbody and his physical body.

2·B

Allow your left palm to come to rest on the
    upper back, your right palm on the
    sacrum.
For perhaps half a minute or more, remain
    present in your stillness. Allow your
    friend to open to trusting your touch.

2·C

When you feel ready, pivot your body and
    lightly pull your hands downward . . .

2·D

. . . separating your hands at
    the waist . . .

[Continued next page]

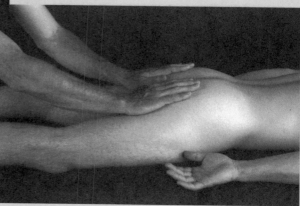

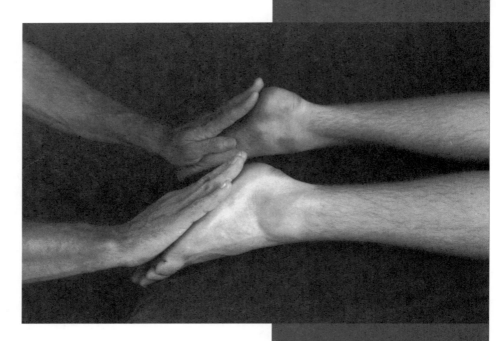

2|·|E . . . continue flowing down the legs and feet . . .

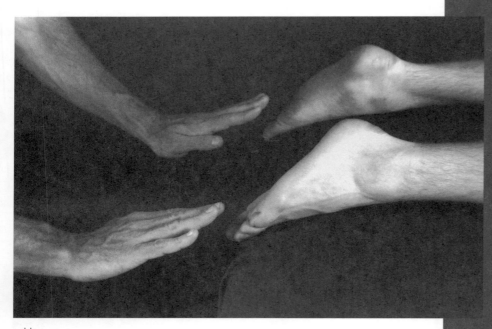

2|·|F

. . . and off the tips of the toes, sensing you are still in contact with
the Godbody at least several inches beyond the toes.

~ If you have feathers or other sensual materials, stroke your friend —
all over — now, before you apply any oil.

3 Spreading Oil

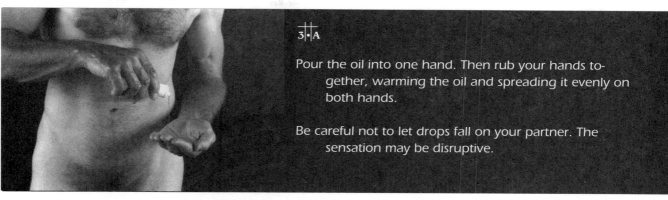

3•A

Pour the oil into one hand. Then rub your hands together, warming the oil and spreading it evenly on both hands.

Be careful not to let drops fall on your partner. The sensation may be disruptive.

3•B

Spread the oil by sliding your hands in a graceful, single stroke up each side in a pulling motion: starting at the feet . . .

3•C ． . . up the legs and the torso . . .

[Continued next page]

At the shoulder, pivot your body and let
your left hand precede your right
hand, sliding down the receiver's
arm . . .

. . . and continuing all the way off the
fingertips.

Always, when sliding off the fingers or
any other part of the body, sense
you are still in contact with the
Godbody at least several inches
beyond the body.

~ Repeat the same sequence on the
other side, reversing the "right"
and "left" instructions and adding
more oil to your hands.
The second part is easier if you first
move to your friend's other side.

This stroke is not the only oil applica-
tion. Generally, you add more oil
to your hands for the initial stroke
of each section.

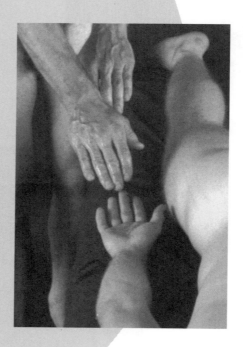

BACK

Your Position: Initially at your friend's head and facing his feet.

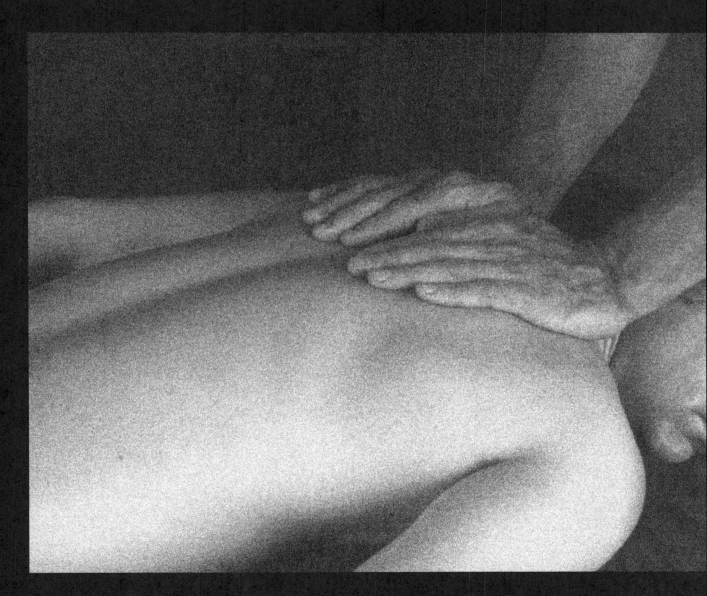

4 Connecting Stroke

4•A

Begin with your hands parallel just below the neck . . .

4•B

. . . and with full hand contact, slide down to the buttocks . . .

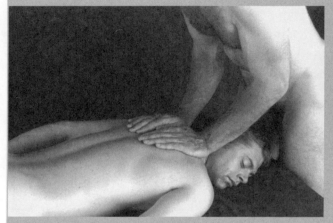

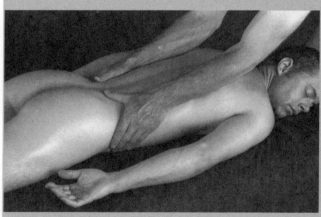

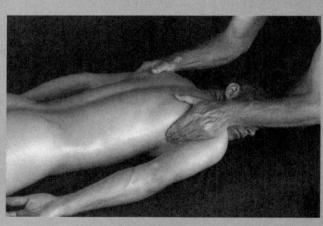

4•C

. . . where you slide your palms outward to the sides of the waist . . .

4•D

. . . and then up the sides toward the underarms . . .

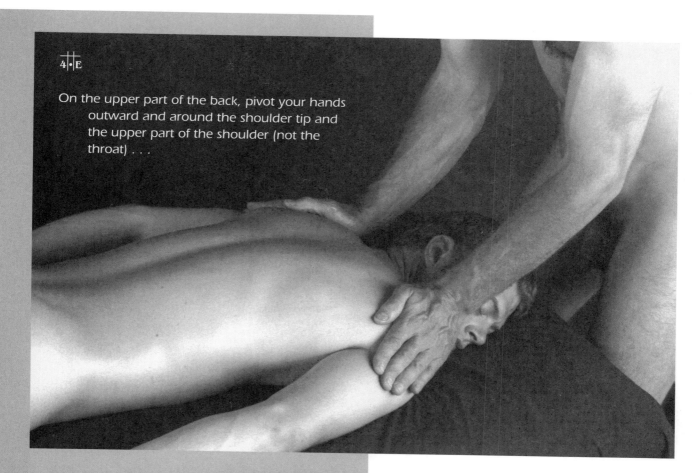

4 • E

On the upper part of the back, pivot your hands outward and around the shoulder tip and the upper part of the shoulder (not the throat) . . .

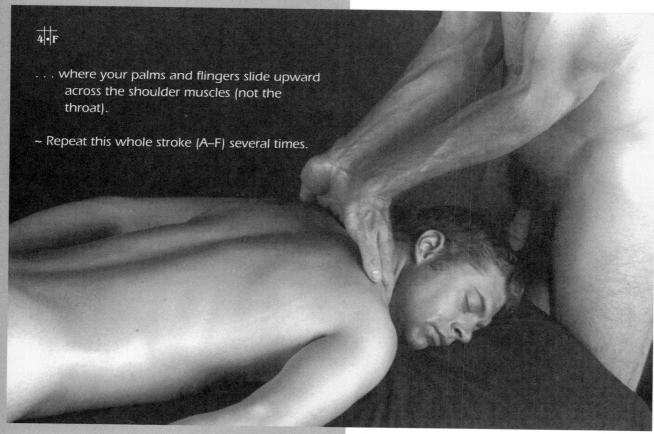

4 • F

. . . where your palms and flingers slide upward across the shoulder muscles (not the throat).

~ Repeat this whole stroke (A–F) several times.

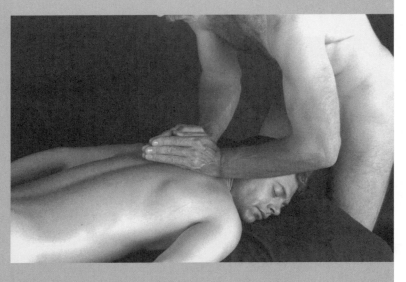

5 Prayer Stroke

 5•A

Just to each side of the spine, starting at the top of the shoulders, slide the soft, outer edge of your palms down the back . . .

5•B

. . . toward the waist . . .

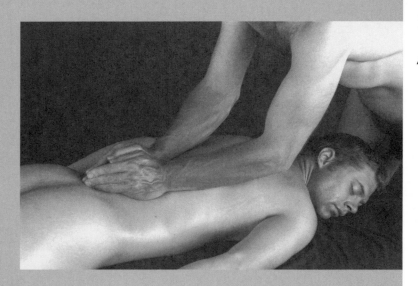

5•C

At the waist, gracefully flatten your palms to slide outward toward the waist . . .

 D

(Now follow the same movements as in the previous stroke, #4.)
When your palms are on the sides of the waist, slide upward to the shoulders . . .

E

On the upper part of the back, pivot your hands outward and
     around the shoulder tips and the upper part of the
     shoulders (not the throat) . . .

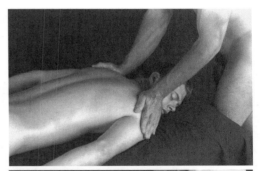

F

. . . where your palms and flingers slide upward across the top
     shoulder muscles (not the throat).

~ Repeat this whole stroke (A–F) several times.

6 Shoulder Strokes

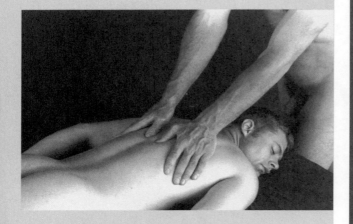

6|·|A

Starting on the lower back, this step is a series of circles gradually coming up the back to the shoulders.

Just to each side of the spine, make circles with the flat parts of your thumbs. Here the thumbs mirror each other: down together, outward from the spine together, etc.

Focus your pressure on your thumbs as you slide toward your friend's feet. The outward and upward parts of the circular movement are light, just to keep a flowing touch.

Remember to let your fingers remain in contact with the back while you emphasize the movement with your thumbs.

6|·|B

B and C

On the right shoulder between the spine and scapula, make circles with your thumbs — this time alternating your hands one after the other.

Again, focus your pressure on your thumbs as you slide downward.

6|·|C

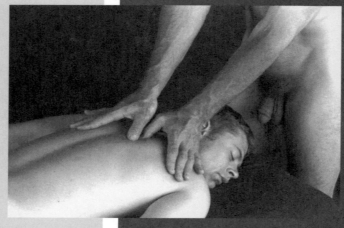

D and E

On the groove between the right scapula and
    clavicle, slide your thumbs outward
    toward the shoulder tip — alternating one
    hand after the other.
Focus your pressure on your thumbs as you
    slide outward, the right hand pushing, the
    left hand pulling.

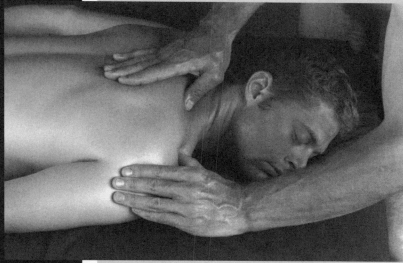

6•D

6•E

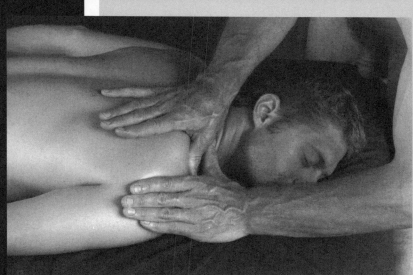

~ Now apply steps B–C and D–E on the
    left shoulder. Substitute "right"
    and "left" for each other in the
    instructions.

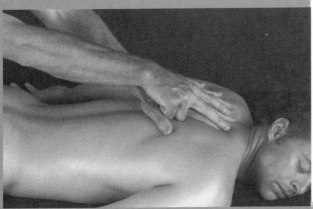

7 Fingers' Pull

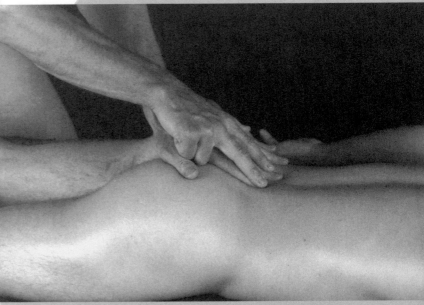

A and B

With a finger pad on each side of the spine at the
   neck, pull downward toward the buttocks.
Use a firm pressure. (You can have even more pressure by putting the fingers of your other hand
   on top of the first, as pictured here.)

~ Repeat this whole stroke several times.

8 Side Pulling

A and B

Alternating your hands on one side, slide them in a
 pulling manner across the side of the torso
 toward the spine.
Starting at the hips, let each succeeding pull begin a
 little higher up the side until the underarms.
 Then gradually come back down to the waist.
Repeat the series several times.

~ Move to the other side, and apply the pulling
 movements to the opposite side.

8·A

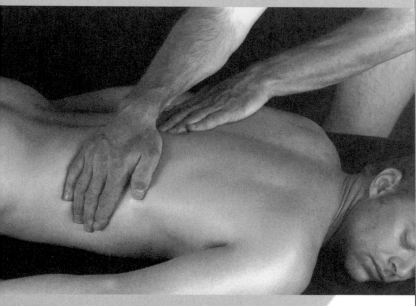

8·B

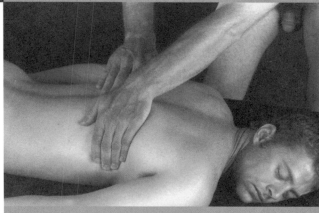

BACK  OF LEGS

Instructions: Written as applied to your friend's left leg.
Your Position: Initially, to the left of your friend's left foot.

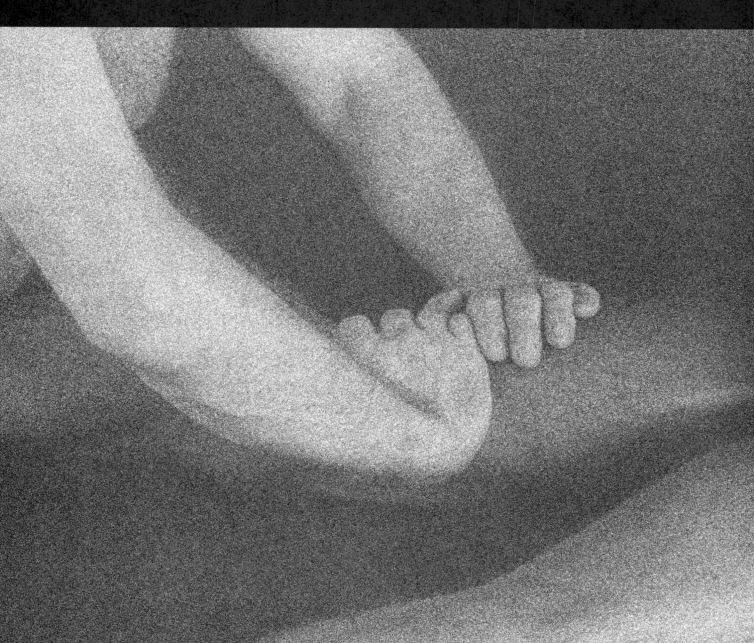

9 Connecting Stroke

9·A

(For both hands, the little-finger side leads.)

With your left hand in front, slide your hands up
the back of the leg, starting at the ankle . . .

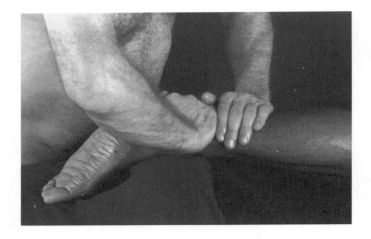

9·B

. . . and continuing up the back of the
leg . . .

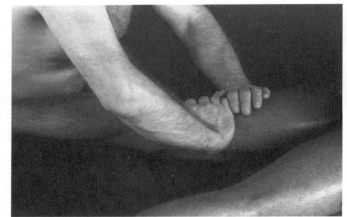

9·C

At the buttocks, let your left hand slide up over
the buttocks and rotate outward at the
waist,
while your right hand rotates into the inner thigh
. . .

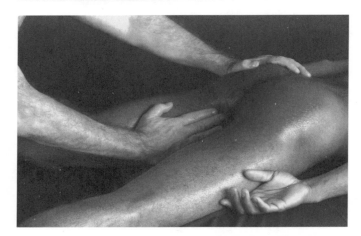

9·D

Continue the slide (in a pulling manner) down the
inner and outer sides of the leg to the ankle.

~ Repeat this whole stroke (A–D) several times.

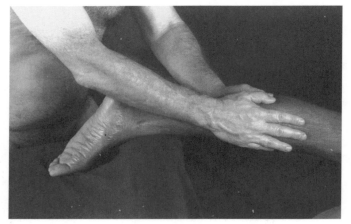

10 Kneading

First focusing on one hand, gently squeeze the muscle with your thumb opposite your fingers (as the left hand is pictured here).

While squeezing, slide a few inches in the direction of your other hand. Then release your squeeze.

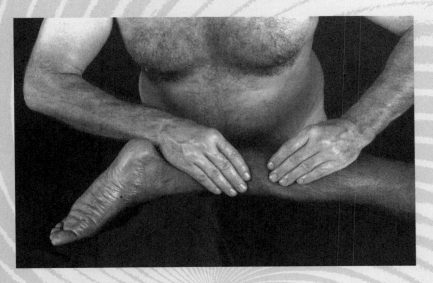

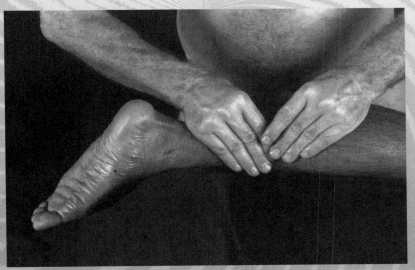

Follow the same pattern with the other hand
(as pictured here: the right hand sliding toward the left).

Alternating your focus on each of your hands, gradually knead the entire calf, thigh, and buttocks.

11 Thumb Slide

11·A

(Let your fingers remain in contact along the sides of the leg. And lighten the pressure in the area behind the knee.)

With your thumbs side-by-side, slide the flats of your thumbs up the middle of the back of the leg from the lower calf . . .

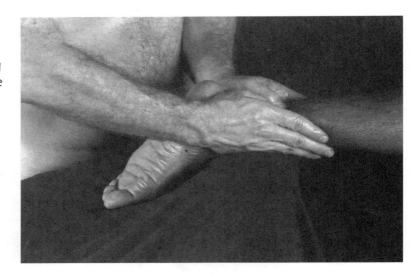

11·B

. . . to the bottom edge of the buttocks.

11·C

At the buttocks, separate your hands and slide them back down the sides of the leg to the ankle.

~ Repeat this whole stroke (A–C) several times.

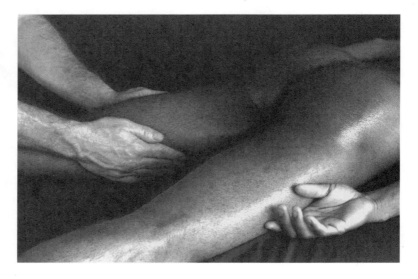

12 "V" Stroke

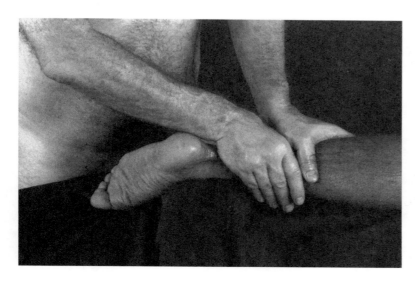

12·A

To make a "V," form both hands as if to shake hands. Then place the left hand above the right hand so that the left thumb is on the right index finger and the left little finger is on the right thumb.

Squeezing the sides of the leg, slide your hands in a V shape up the back of the leg from the lower calf . . .

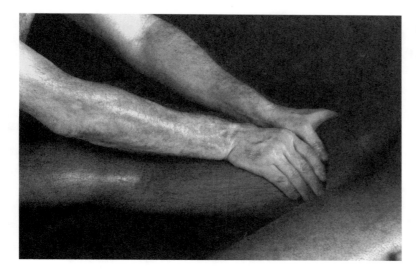

12·B

. . . to the bottom edge of the buttocks . . .

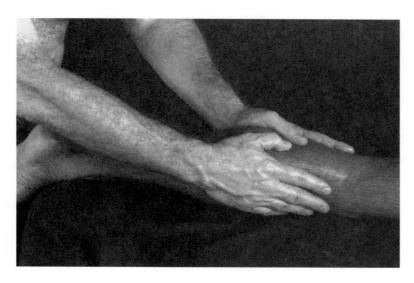

12·C

At the buttocks, separate your hands and slide them back down the sides of the leg to the ankle (as in the previous stroke, #11).

~ Repeat this whole stroke (A–C) several times.

14 Back-of-Leg Feather Stroke

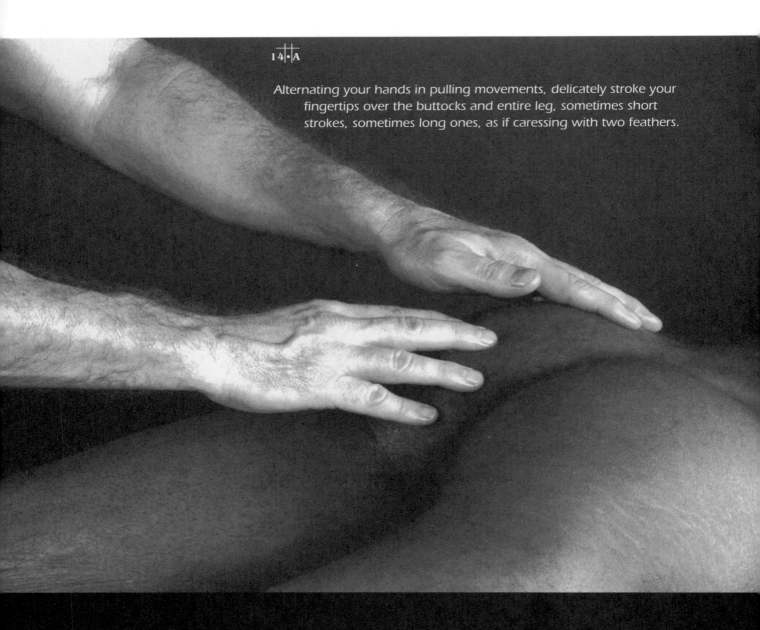

14•A

Alternating your hands in pulling movements, delicately stroke your fingertips over the buttocks and entire leg, sometimes short strokes, sometimes long ones, as if caressing with two feathers.

15 Follow the same sequence on the right leg (#9 – #14)

Move to your friend's other side and reverse the right- and left-hand positions in the instructions.

BACK SIDE Conclusion

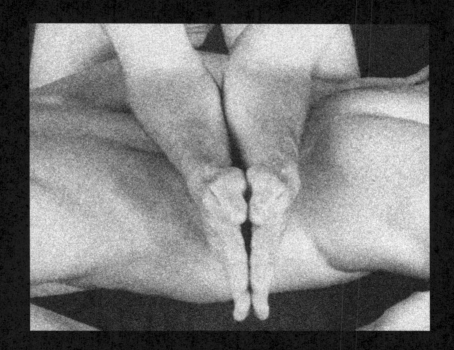

16 Back Hug

16•A

(This may be a difficult stroke unless you are using a massage table.)

Beginning at your friend's lower back . . .

16•B

. . . as soon as possible, rotate your forearms so that the soft, inner side of the forearms are contacting the spine as you slide your forearms in opposite directions . . .

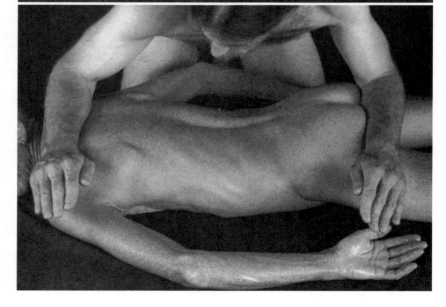

16•C

. . . to below the buttocks and to the upper back.
Lighten your pressure significantly as you reach the neck area.
Then reverse your movement so that you apply a firm pressure
. . .

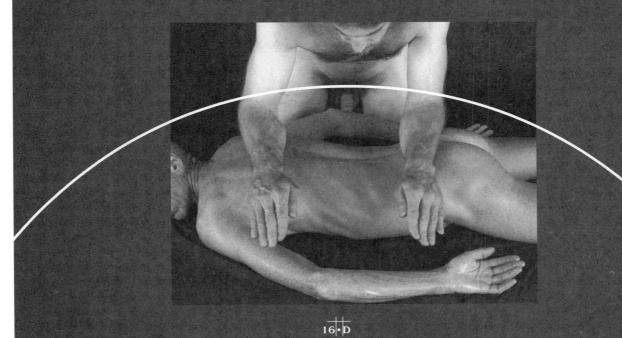

16·D

. . . as you slide the soft, inner side of your forearms back together.
When your forearms come close together (as in step A), you will need to rotate them so the edges of one
of your forearm bones do not come in contact with the spine. Be very light here so not to cause
bone-against-bone bumping and discomfort.

~ Repeat A–D several times, and on the final outward movement . . .

16·E

. . . rest your chest on your friend's back for perhaps a half a minute or longer.
When you feel complete, slowly lift up, off your friend, and move into the next stroke.

(Be very careful not to put pressure on the neck and throat area.)
Allow this embrace to Be Here Now. Feel your connection with
your friend's heart, his body, and Godbody.

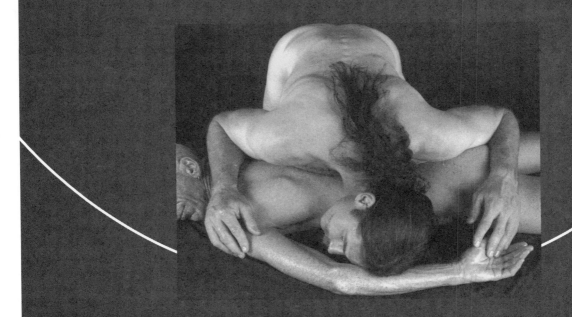

17 Concluding Stroke

17·A   In one long movement, slowly slide your hands up from the feet . . .

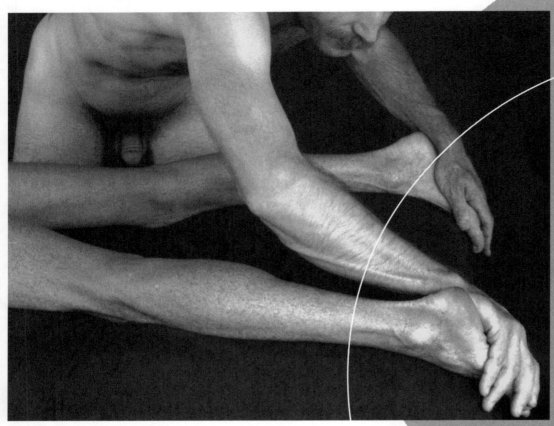

17·B   . . . over the legs, buttocks, and back . . .

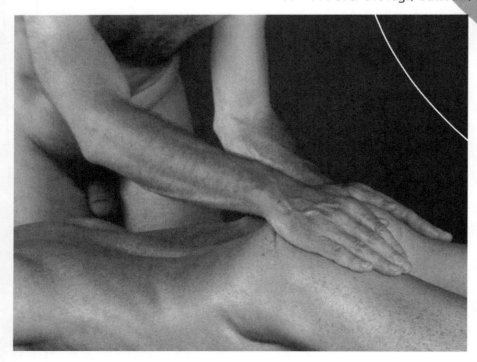

. . . to the shoulder, and then pushing down the arms . . .

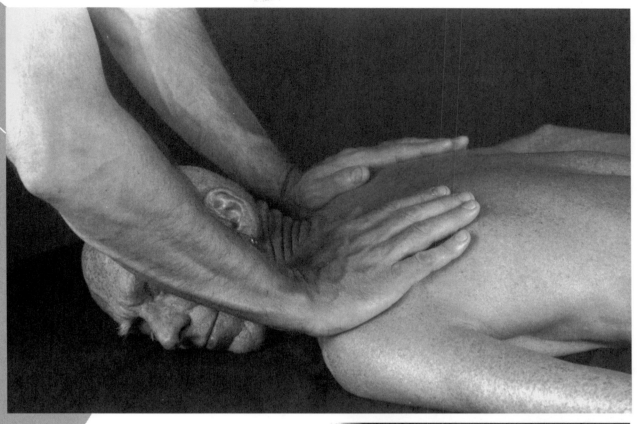

. . . to the hands . . .

. . . and slowly and smoothly off the fingertips, as if
continuing to stroke the Godbody.

If you wish, then gently feather stroke with your
fingertips the entire back side.

~ After a while, with a gentle voice, invite your friend
to turn over on to his back when he is ready.

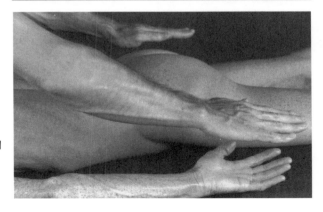

ARMS

Instructions: Written as applied to the right arm.
Friend's Position: Lying on back with arms by side.
Your Position: Initially at the right waist, facing the head.

18 Connecting Stroke

18·A

First, gently hold his right wrist in your right
    hand. Then, with the little-finger side
    leading, slide your left hand up the outside
    of the right arm.

18·B

Pivot on the shoulder tip . . .

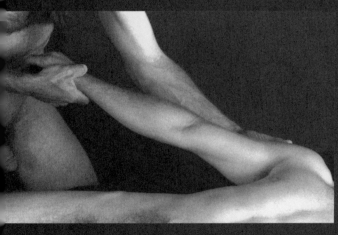

18·C

. . . and slide down on the back side of the arm . . .

18·D

. . . to the wrist.

18•E

Now hold the wrist away
    from his body with
    your left hand . . .

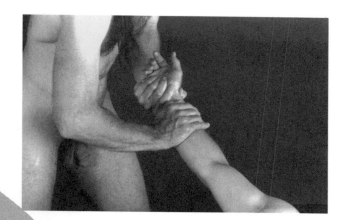

18•F

. . . and slide your right hand up the inside of the
    right arm with your little-finger side leading.
Just before the underarm, pivot your right hand to
    the underside of the shoulder . . .

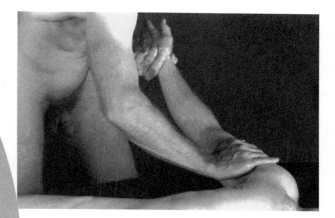

18•G

. . . and slide downward on the back side of the arm . . .

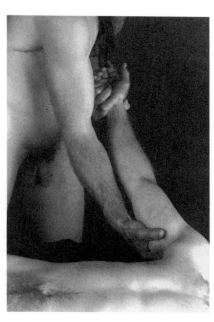

18•H

. . . to the wrist.

~ Repeat this whole stroke (A–H)
    several times.

19 Upper Arm Stroke

19•A

Hold your friend's right hand against your left
   rib cage with your left inner arm.

Slide your right hand upward toward the
   shoulder on the inside of his upper arm
while your left hand holds the underside of
   your friend's elbow.

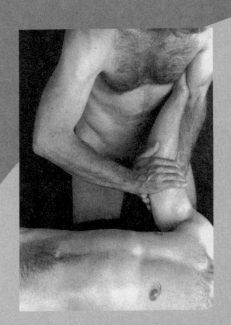

19•B

Your right hand rotates at the underarm . . .

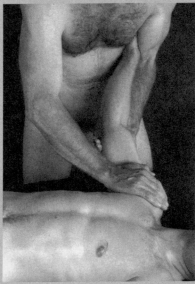

19•C

. . . and slides downward on the underside.
At the same time, your left hand rotates at the
   elbow and slides upward on the upper
   side of the upper arm.

Your left hand rotates outward on the shoulder . . .

. . . and slides downward on the back side of the upper arm.

As your left hand approaches the elbow, continue with step A: your right hand rotates at the elbow and slides upward . . .

~ Repeat this whole stroke (A–E) several times.

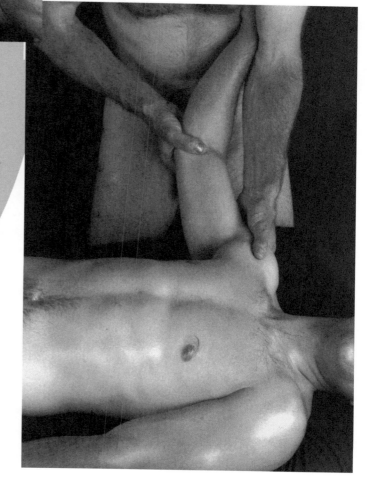

20 Forearm Stroke

20•A

Holding the forearm upright with your abdomen, slide the flat
sides of your thumbs down the inside of the forearm.
Let your thumbs be parallel with each other.

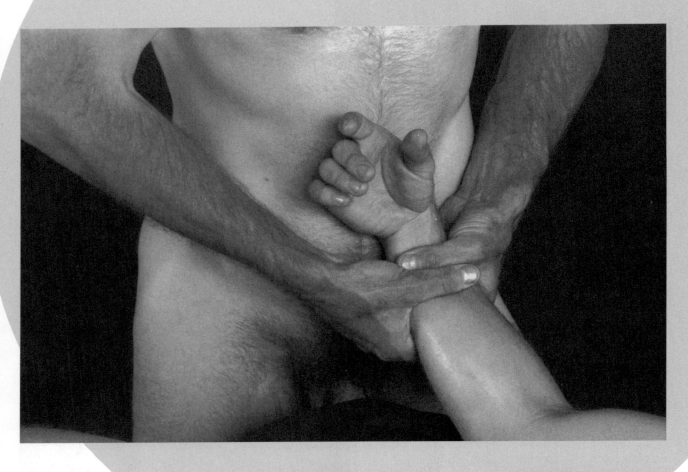

20•B

When your thumbs reach
the inner side of the elbow,
lighten your touch and slide your
hands back up to the wrist.

~ Repeat A–B several times and continue
with the right hand (next section)
before massaging the left arm.

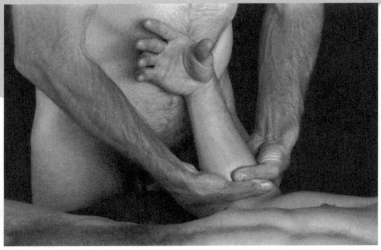

HANDS

Instructions: Written as applied to the right hand.

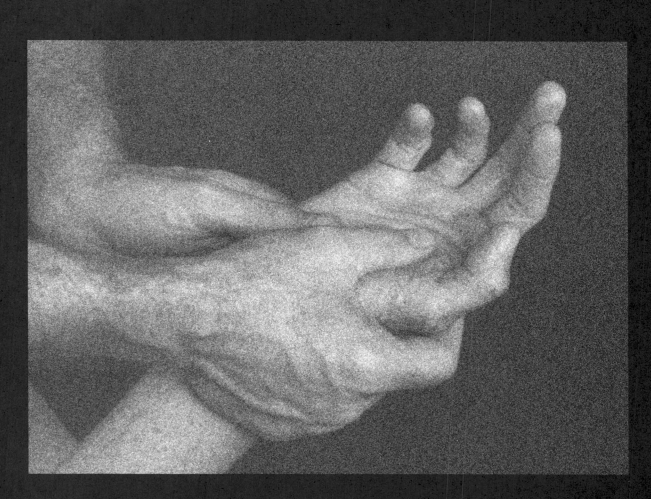

21 Hand Curl

A and B
On the back side of your friend's hand, firmly slide the fleshy heel-part of your thumbs
    outward to the sides of the hand while curling the hand inward.
~ Repeat this stroke several times.

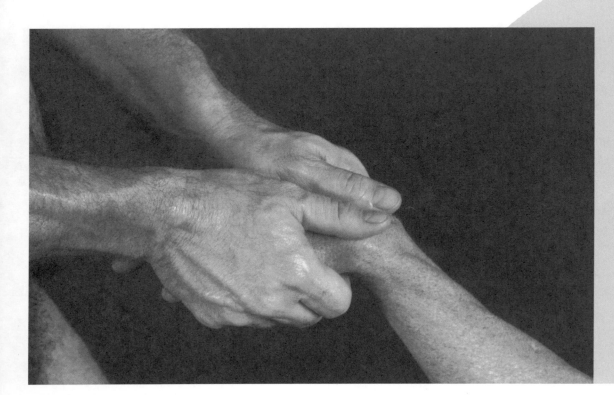

21 · A

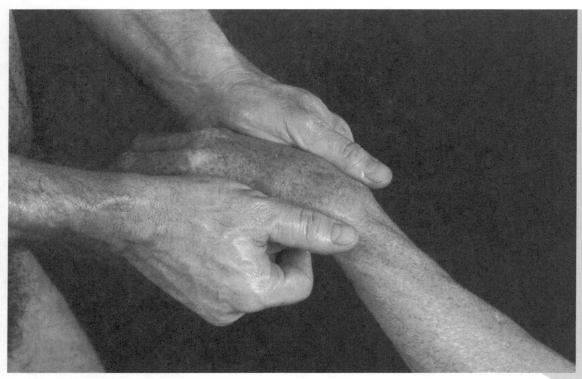

21 · B

22 Palm Massage

A and B

Alternating your thumbs, firmly push your thumb pads upward on the palm.

(Massage only with pushing strokes here. Use no pressure when sliding your thumbs back to begin the
   pushing.)

~ Repeat the movements many times, covering the palm entirely.

22·A

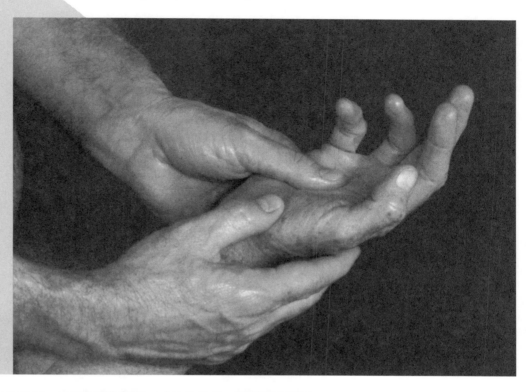

22·B

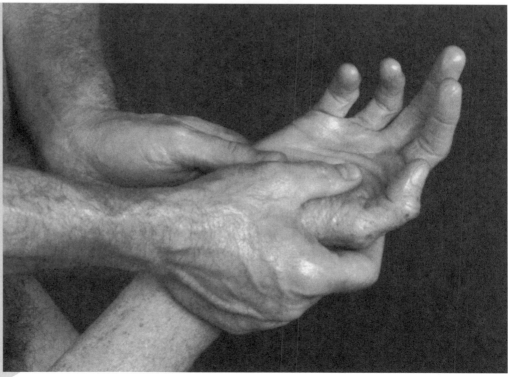

23 Web Stroke

23·A

With your right thumb and curled index finger between your friend's
right thumb and first finger . . .

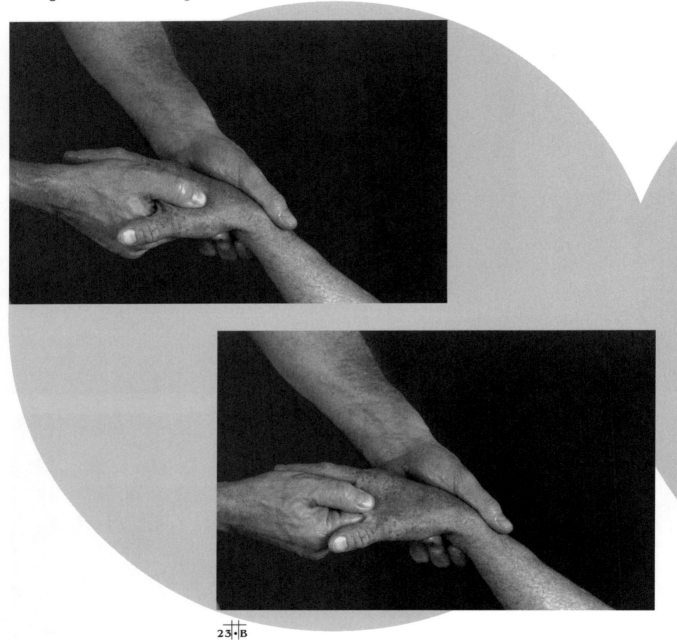

23·B

. . . slide outward firmly — but without too much pressure.
(Use no pressure when sliding your thumbs back to begin the pulling
movement.)

~ Repeat this stroke several times.

24 Finger Stroke

24·A

Starting at the tip of your friend's finger . . .

24·B

. . . slide very lightly down the sides of the finger with your thumb and finger — very, very lightly.

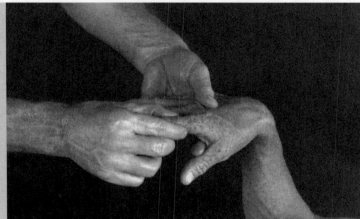

24·C

Grasping the finger firmly at its base . . .

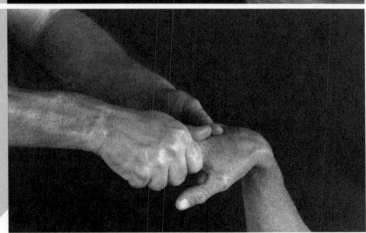

24·D

. . . slide up and off the finger.

~ Repeat A–D once on the thumb and once on each finger.

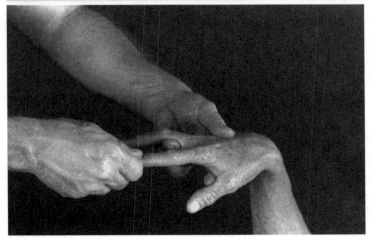

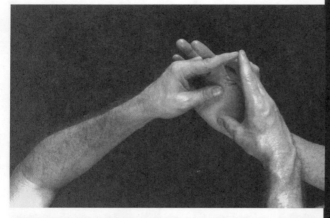

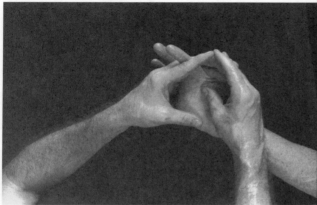

25 Palm Reading

A and B

Interlacing your fingers with your friend's,
stretch his palm open and lightly stroke
the palm with your thumb tips — very,
very, very lightly as if your thumbs
were feathers.
(Feathering from the heel of the hand up to
the base of the fingers is usually the
most effective method.)

26

Repeat: Arm Connecting Stroke (#18)

27 Arm and Hand Feather Stroke

(No illustration)
Alternating your hands in a pulling movement, delicately stroke your fingertips over the entire arm
and hand — sometimes short strokes, sometimes
long ones on your friend's arm resting on the
table (or bed).

28

**Follow the same Arm and Hand sequence on the
left arm**

Remember to reverse your right- and left-hand
instructions.

FRONT OF LEGS

Instructions: Written as applied to the right leg.

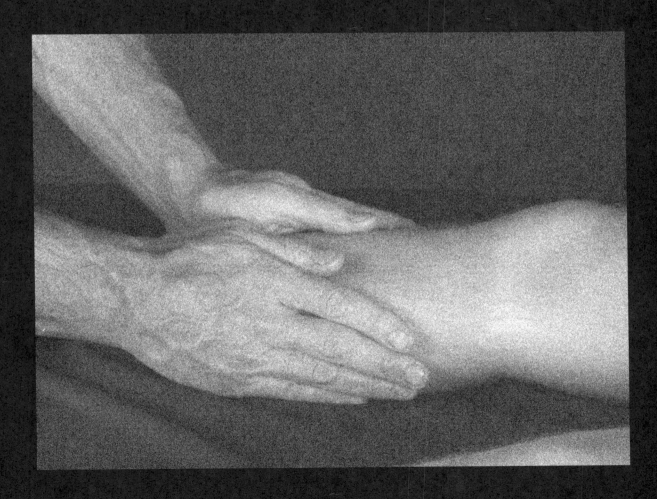

29 Connecting Stroke

29•A

With your left hand leading . . .

(For both hands, the little-finger side leads; the thumbs are beside the index fingers.)

29•B

. . . slide your hands up the front of the leg.

29•C

Near the pelvis, rotate your hands outward . . .

29•D

. . . and slide down the inner and outer sides of the leg to the ankle.

~ Repeat this whole stroke (A–D) several times.

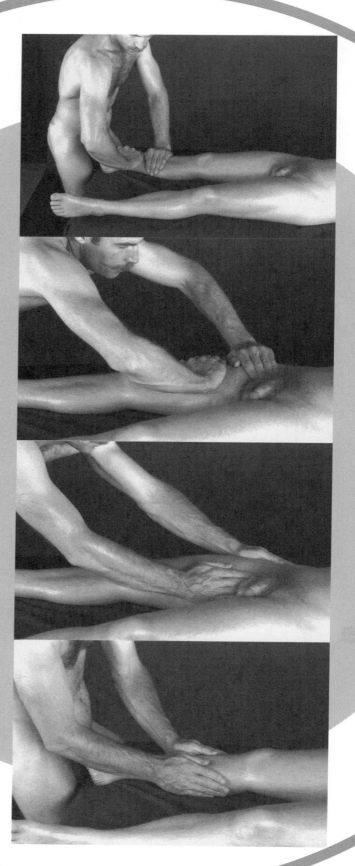

30 Mini-Connecting Stroke

A through C

On the thigh, make a series of short connecting strokes similar to the previous
   stroke (#29) but only on the thigh and
   only about six inches long.
Each succeeding stroke starts a little farther
   up the thigh until the whole length of
   the thigh is covered.

~ Repeat this whole series several times.

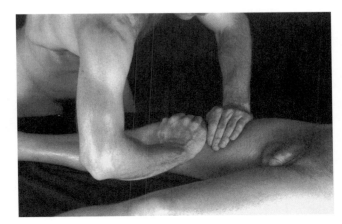
30•A

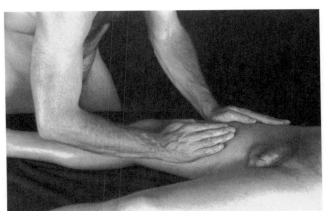
30•B

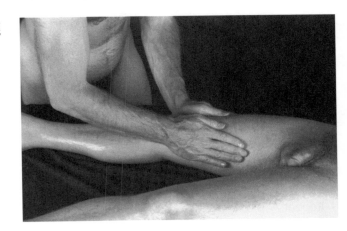
30•C

First, focusing on your right hand, gently squeeze
the thigh muscles between your thumb and
your fingers. While squeezing, slide a few
inches in the direction of your other hand and
release your squeeze.

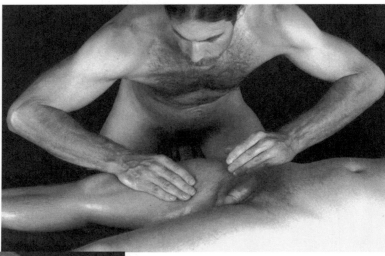

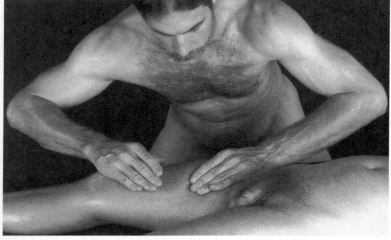

31|•B

Then, follow the same pattern with your left hand.

~ Repeat A–B to gradually knead the entire front thigh.

32   Repeat: Front-of-Leg Connecting Stroke (#29)

Continue with the right foot before massaging the left leg.

FEET

Instruction: Written as applied to the right foot.

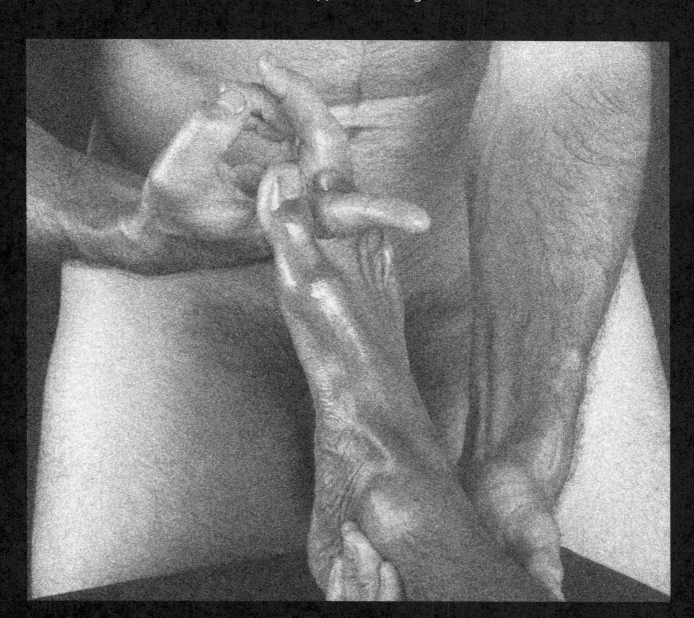

33 Ankle Circling

A and B

With your flat fingers, stroke in circular movements
around the ankle several times.

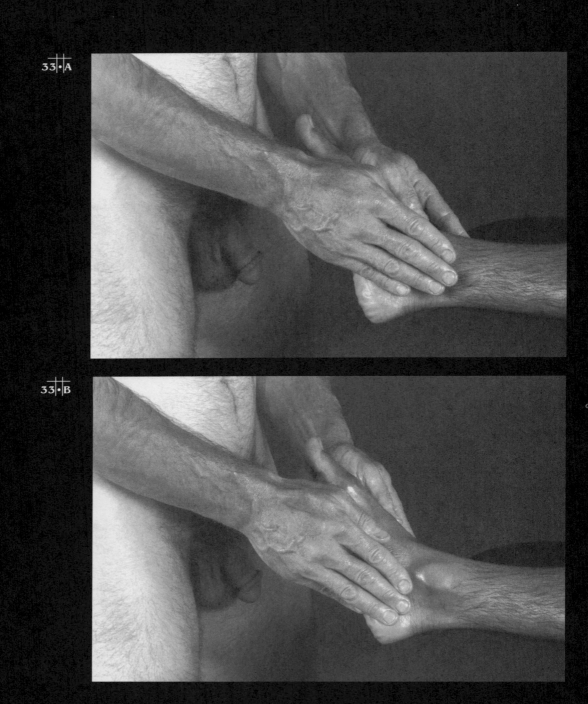

33•A

33•B

34 Connecting Stroke

A and B

Alternating your hands, squeeze the foot and slide
    off the end.

~ Repeat this stroke several times.

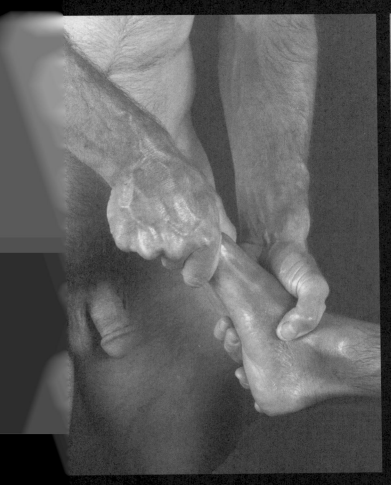

34•A

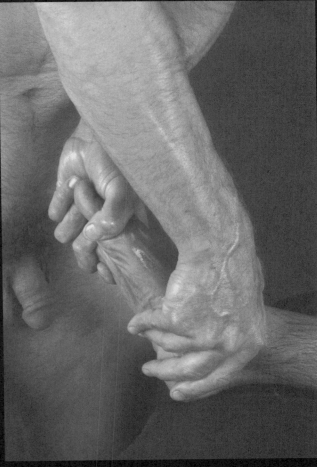

34•B

35 Arc de Triomphe

A and B

Firmly slide the heel of your right hand downward on the arch.
(The ankle rests in your left hand.)

~ Repeat this stroke several times.

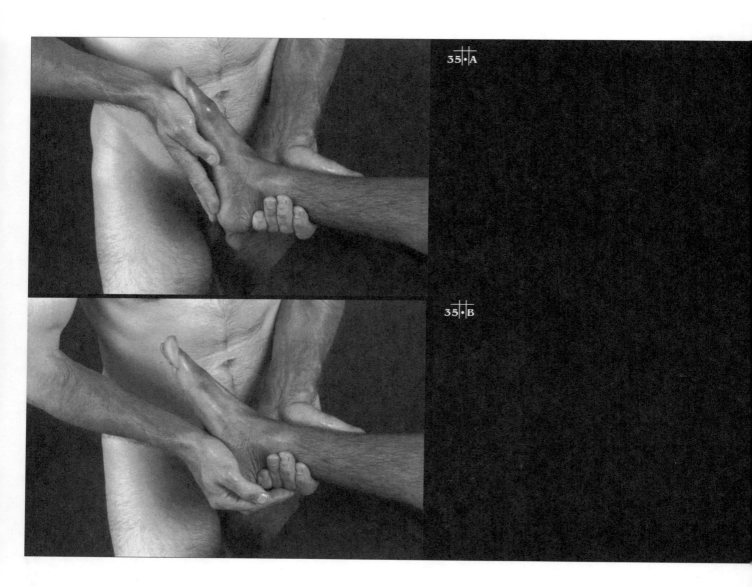

36 Finger Circles

On the top of the foot, make small circles with your
     finger pads — not the pointed edges of your
     fingertips.
(Either slide your fingers over the skin and/or, with a
     little more pressure, slide your friend's skin over
     the muscles, tendons, and bones beneath.)

~ Repeat these circles over the entire top of the foot.

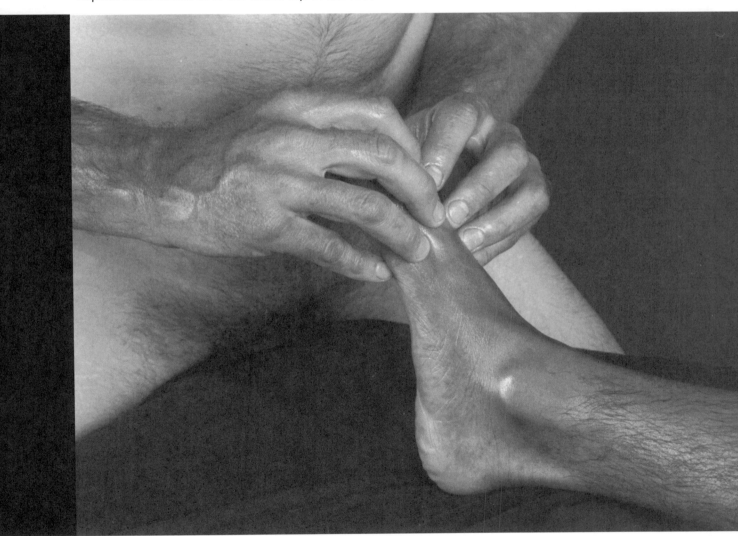

37 Between-the-Toes Stroke

A and B

With your right-hand index finger on top on the right foot and your right-hand thumb on the bottom, squeeze and slide up and down several times between each of the toes.

37•A

37•B

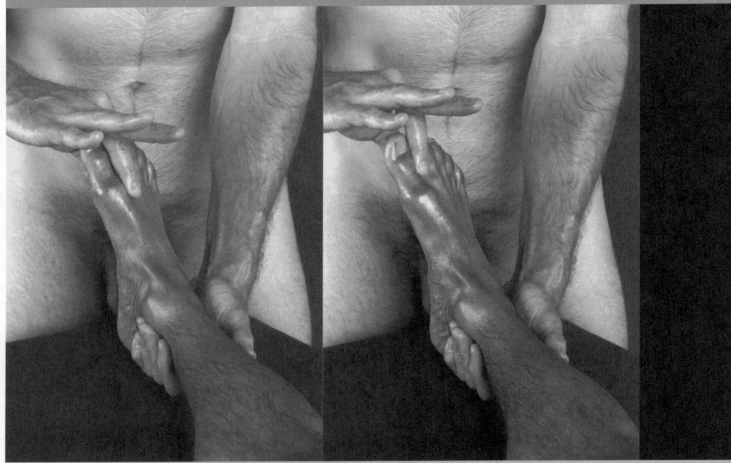

38 Slithering

A and B

Very slowly and gently "screw" any right finger in
and out between each set of toes.

38·A

38·B

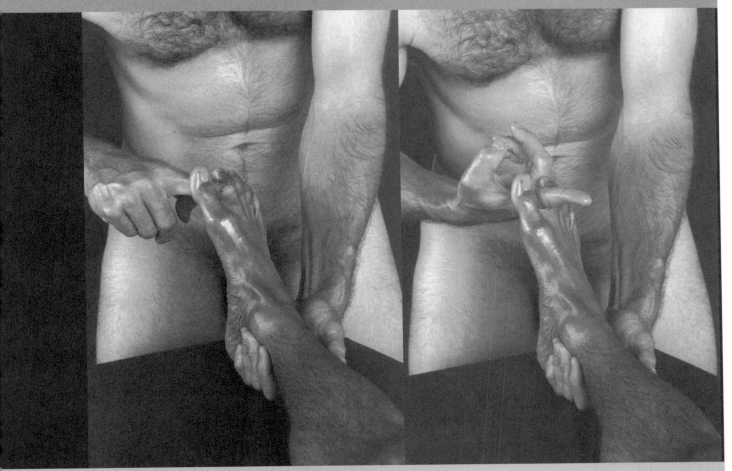

39

Repeat: Front-of-Leg Connecting Stroke (#29)

40 Leg and Foot Feather Stroke

Alternating your hands in a pulling movement,
delicately stroke your fingertips over the
entire leg and foot — sometimes short
strokes, sometimes long ones.

41

**Follow the same Front-of-Legs and Feet sequence
on the left leg**

Remember to reverse your right- and left-hand
instructions.

FRONT TORSO

Your Position: Initially at your friend's right side.

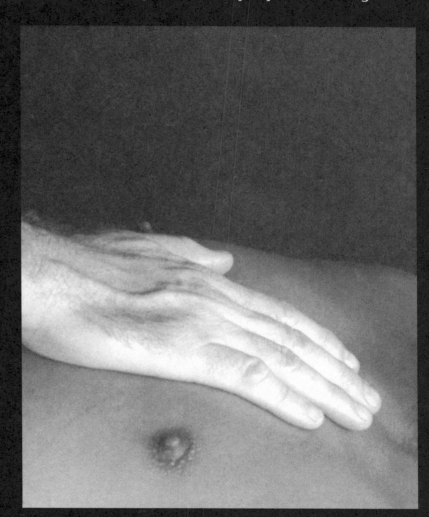

First, on the soft abdominal cavity, practice your right-
and left-hand movements separately.

42 ▪ 1

Your right hand strokes a half circle on the lower part
of the abdomen starting on your friend's left side
. . .

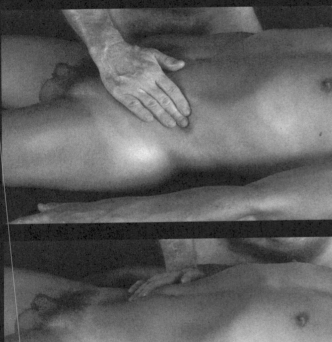

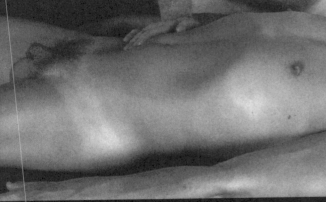

42 ▪ 2

. . . and pulling across (a little down, then a little up) to
your friend's right side.

42•3

Your left hand strokes a full circle around the whole abdomen, starting at the upper right side of the abdomen . . .

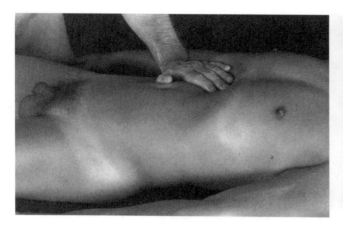

42•4

. . . and pushing across (a little up, then a little down) to the left side . . .

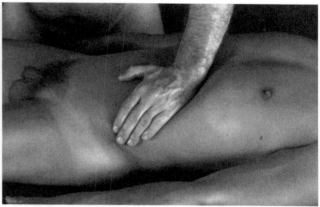

42•5

. . . where, continuing, your left hand rotates and begins a pulling movement (just as the left hand has done) . . .

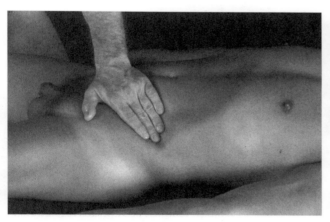

42•6

. . . across the lower abdomen (a little down, then a little up) to your friend's right side.
(Here, continuing without stopping, your left hand pivots into pushing up and across the upper abdomen as in the beginning of the left-hand part.)

[Continued next page]

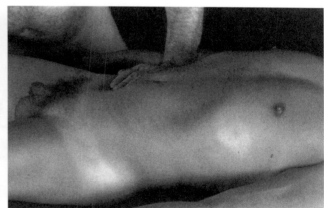

Moon Stroke ▪ complete version

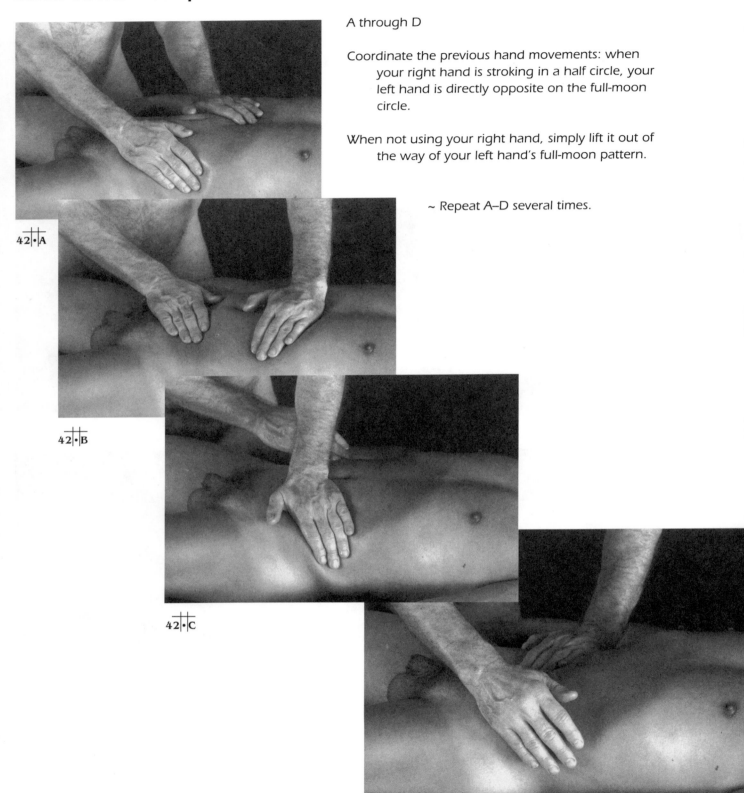

42│•│A

42│•│B

42│•│C

42│•│D

A through D

Coordinate the previous hand movements: when your right hand is stroking in a half circle, your left hand is directly opposite on the full-moon circle.

When not using your right hand, simply lift it out of the way of your left hand's full-moon pattern.

~ Repeat A–D several times.

43 Center Slide

A and B

Alternating your hands, firmly and slowly slide them
up the midline from the lower abdomen to the
upper chest.

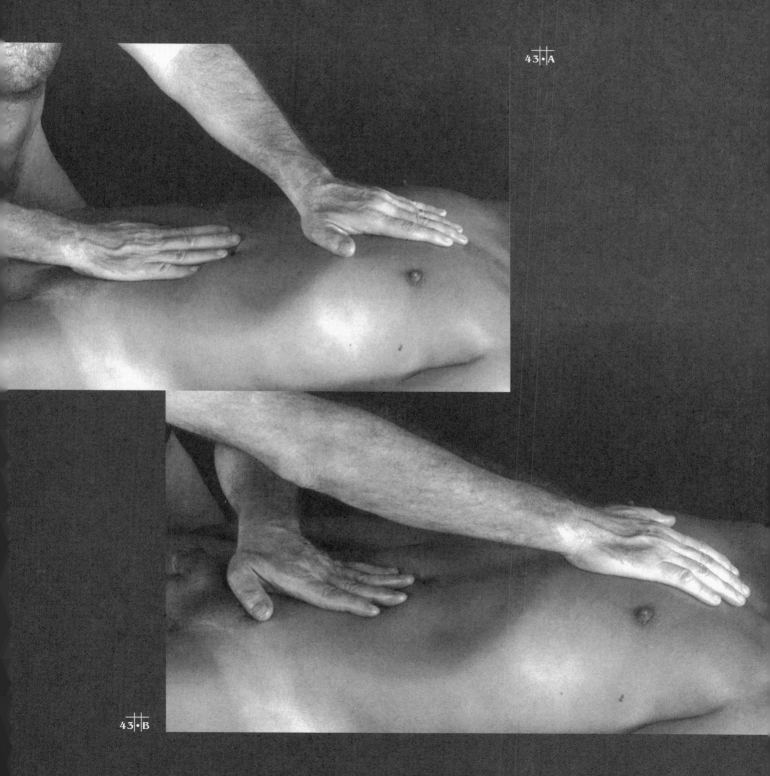

43 • A

43 • B

44   Side Pulling

A and B

Alternating your hands, slide them in a pulling
　　　manner across the side of the torso toward the
　　　front midline.
Repeat several times this series which begins at the
　　　hips and gradually moves up to the underarms
　　　and back down.
Be quite firm on the pects in the upper chest area.

~ Move to the other side, and apply the pulling
　　　movements to the opposite side.

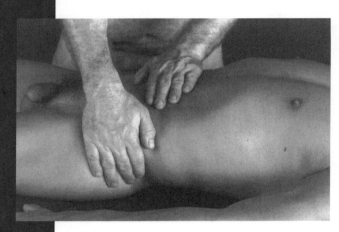

44•A

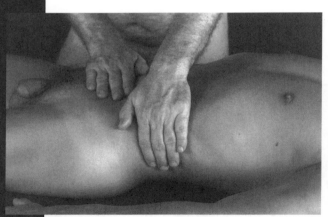

44•B

45 Spokes Stroke

A and B

Imagine the nipple as the axis in a wheel with spokes radiating out from the axis.

Using the pads of the index fingers and thumbs of both hands, gently squeeze at the axis and slide out along a spoke, moving your hands in opposite directions.

~ Repeat this pattern several times along the different spokes.

45•A

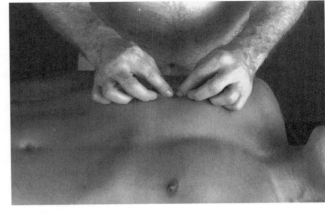

45•B

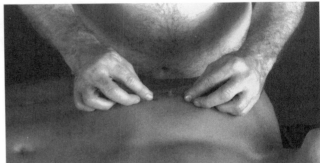

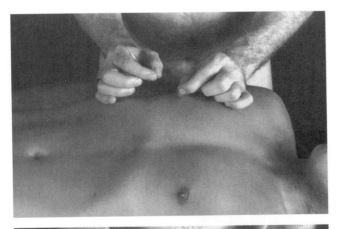

45•C

C and D

Gently squeeze the base of the nipple between the pads of your index finger and thumb of one hand and slide straight up and off the nipple.

Continue this pattern, alternating your hands one immediately after the other.

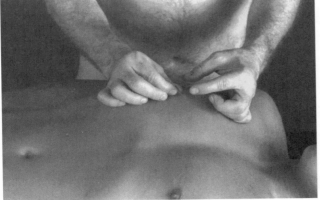

~ Now move to the other side and repeat this stroke on the other nipple.

45•D

Alternating your hands in
a pulling movement,
delicately stroke your
fingertips over the
entire torso.

Include and begin to
focus on the genital
and thigh areas in
preparation for the
genital strokes next.

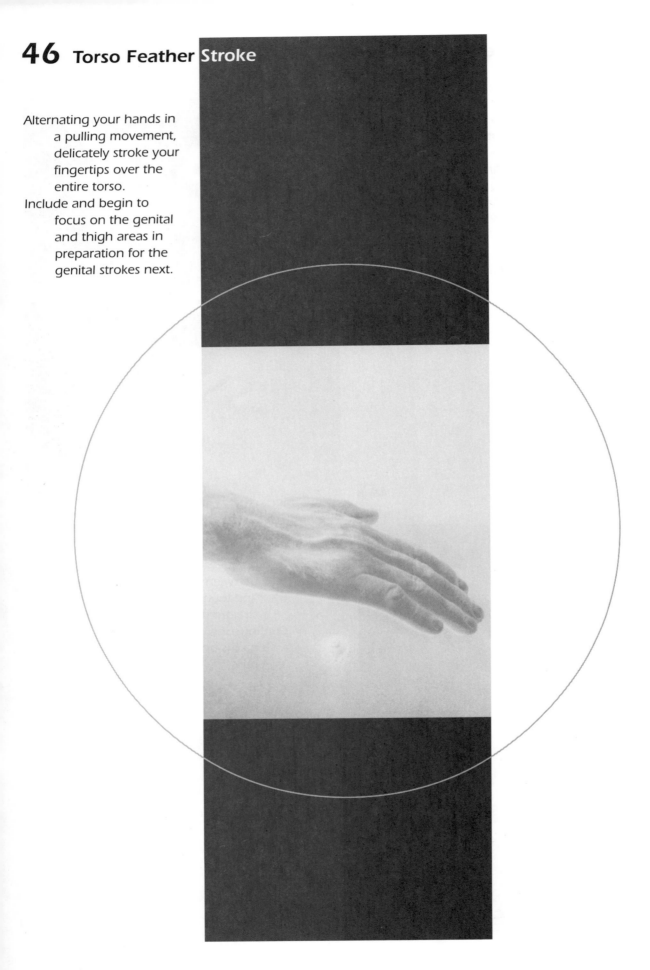

GENITALS

Friend's Position: Lying on back.
Your Position: To his right side.

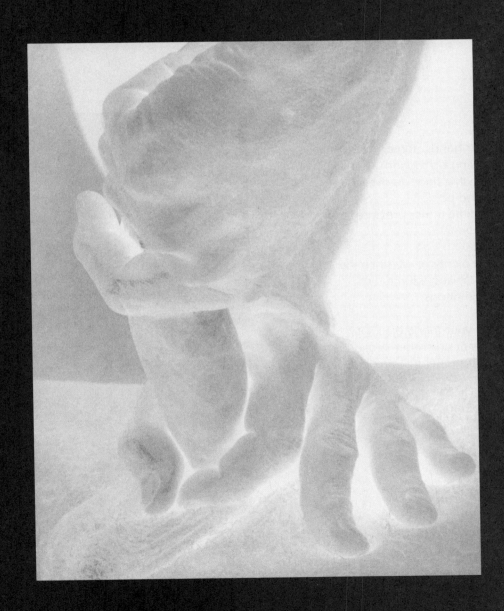

47 Anointing with Oil

47|•|A

Let your left hand, with fingers slightly
spread, rest on the scrotum and
underneath side of the penis.
Then with your right hand, pour oil on
the back of your left hand so that
the oil seeps through your fingers.

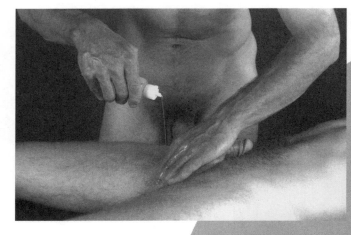

B and C

Alternating your hands, spread the oil
with a pulling up motion, sliding
from the pelvic floor up over the
scrotum and penis.
Perhaps give a little firmer pressure on
the pelvic floor.

Be sure there is plenty of oil, since the
following strokes assume well-
lubricated motions.

~ Note: Should your friend ejaculate
during this or any other stroke,
perhaps go to "Being," stroke #53.

48 The Juicer

A and B

Your left hand gently stretches the foreskin down
along the shaft of the flaccid or erect penis.
Your right hand points as if to twist a halved orange
on a juicer.
Concentrating on the head of the penis, rotate your
right-hand fingers back and forth in coordina-
tion with an up-and-down sliding motion.

Vary the amount of pressure from your right hand.

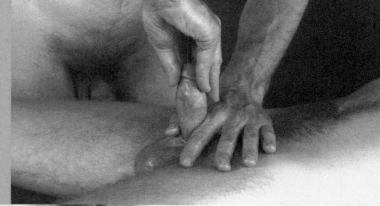

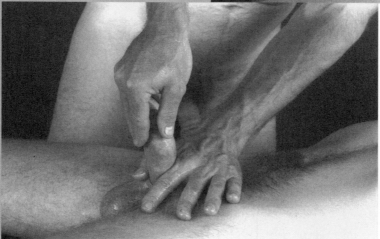

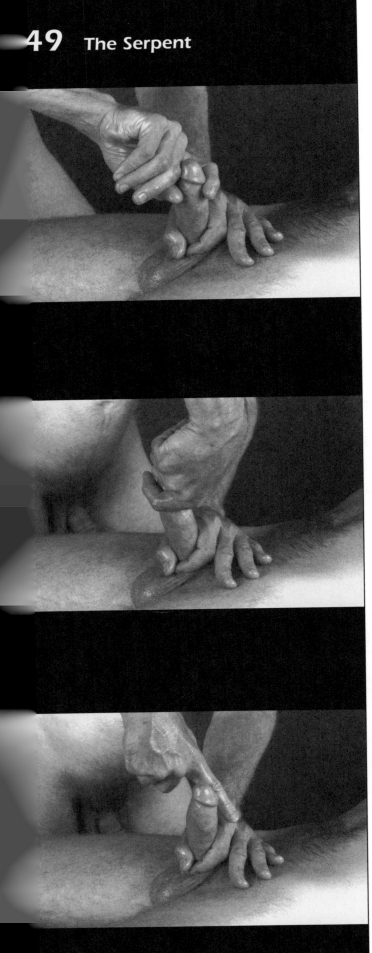

49•A

Your left hand gently stretches the foreskin down along the shaft of the flaccid or erect penis.

Your right thumb and index finger form a circle just below the head of the penis . . .

49•B

. . . and rotate in a clockwise direction as far as your wrist permits.

49•C

Continuing the movement, fold your right thumb so that your index finger can maintain contact in the rotation (until the thumb can form a circle with the index finger again around the head of the penis, as in step A).

~ Repeat this circling several times.

50 The Countdown

Using plenty of oil and alternating your hands,
make one upward stroke with your left hand
. . .

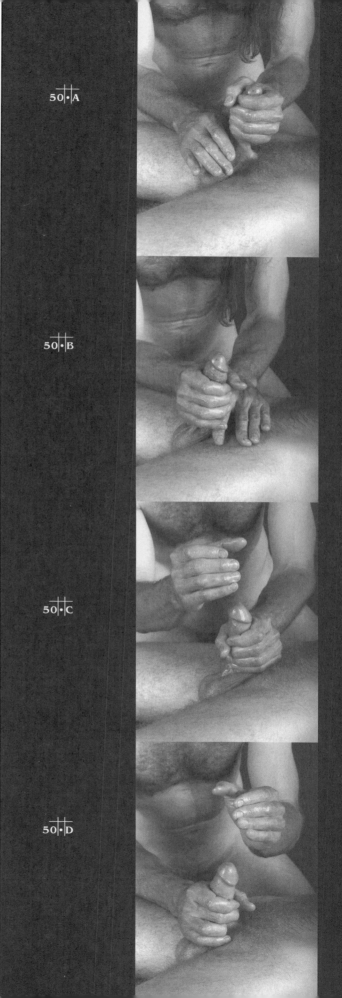

50•A

. . . immediately followed by your right hand . . .
then the left hand, etc., up to ten upward
strokes.

50•B

C and D: On an erect or semierect penis

When the penis is erect or semierect, the following
downward stroking is usually easier than on
a flaccid penis. (Both methods can feel
wonderful.)

Starting above the head of the penis, slide your
encircling hand down the head and shaft.
The other hand immediately follows the same
pattern until ten downward strokes are
completed.

[Continued next page]

50•C

50•D

E and F: On a flaccid penis

When the penis is flaccid, downward stroking is usually easier by
    laying the penis backward on the lower abdomen and stroking
    with alternating, slightly cupped palms and fingers on the
    underside of the shaft.
The hands alternate until ten downward strokes are completed.

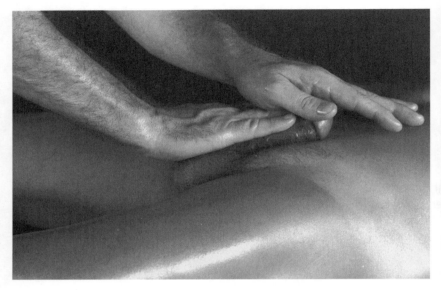

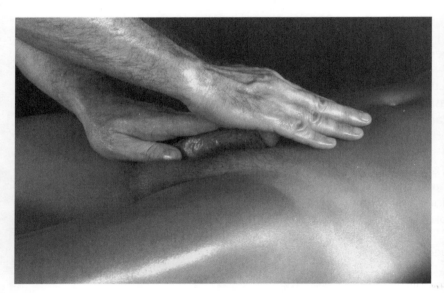

■ ■ ■ **For any degree of erection or flaccidity**, continue The Count-
    down with nine upward, nine downward, eight upward, eight
    downward — all the way to one up and one down.
Should your friend ejaculate, let him relax into the afterglow by
    doing "Being," stroke #53.

Suggestion: Syncopate the rhythm of your stroking. Rather than
    using an even beat (1-2-3-4-5-6), wait a moment after each set
    of two strokes (1-2—3-4—5-6).

51 The Scrotum Ring

A and B

Your right thumb along with your right index and
        perhaps middle fingers encircle the scrotum.
        (Be careful not to squeeze the testicles.)

Then your right hand massages the muscles beneath
        the scrotum as you slide your right hand up
        and down while your left hand strokes up and
        down on the flaccid or erect penile shaft.

~ Vary the amount of pressure of your right hand
        against the base of the penis as you repeat this
        stroke several times.

51•A

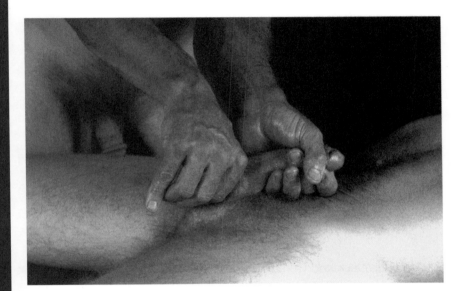

51•B

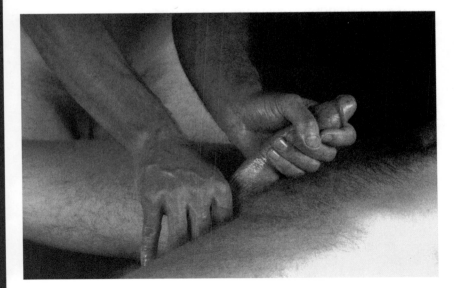

52 Feelin' Good All Over

In this series of strokes, you connect the enjoyable sensations of the genitals with the enjoyable sensations of other parts of the body — if your friend still wishes more genital stimulation.

These strokes are not illustrated since they can be free-form with many variations that you and your friend enjoy.

The following are some wonderful possibilities. Explore, adapt, invent as you wish. Celebrate the physical body and the Godbody.

A. Abdomen and Genitals

While your right hand massages the penis in any fashion, your left hand kneads or makes circular strokes on the abdomen.
(For a description of kneading, see stroke #10.)

B. Chest and Genitals

As your right hand strokes the penis, your left hand firmly massages the right side of the chest area, perhaps followed by delicate nipple caressing.

C. Shoulder/Neck and Genitals

While your right hand continues on the penis, knead the right shoulder and neck muscles with your left hand.
Be careful not to squeeze the throat.

D. Inner Thigh and Genitals

Now your hands change positions: Your left slides down to massage the penis while your right hand kneads the right inner thigh.

E. Change Sides

If it is possible, move to the other side and follow the same sequence while simply reversing the left- and right-hand instructions.

If you cannot easily move to the over side, modify your stroking so that the left chest/nipple, neck/shoulder, and thigh areas are massaged also.

Once you complete this series, move back to your friend's right side for the following instructions.

53 Being

With your right hand embracing your friend's
    scrotum and penis, gently bring your left hand
    to rest on your friend's heart area.
For maybe half a minute or longer, go inside to your
    heart and feel your connection with your
    friend, his physical body, his Godbody.

Leaving your right hand in the same place on the
    scrotum, slowly lift your left hand and allow it
    to rest on your friend's head such that your
    palm is on the forehead and your fingers are
    on the center top of the head.
Now imagine a flow of energy moving between
    your palms along an imaginary axis through
    the core of your friend.
Give a soft verbal invitation to your friend to take a
    slightly fuller inhalation and to imagine the
    breath beginning at the floor of his pelvis and
    coming up the core of the body to the top of
    his head.
For the exhalation, invite him to simply let go of the
    breath and to imagine the breath reversing
    and flowing from the top of his head, down
    through the core of his being, and out the
    floor of his pelvis.

Continue this breathing and imaging guidance for
    perhaps two to five minutes. Rather than
    watching the clock, simply allow a completion
    to unfold.

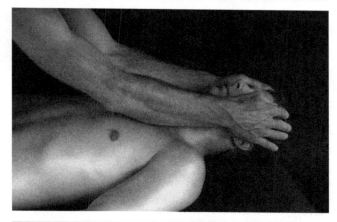

Now feather stroke with the tips of your fingers from
    the top of the head . . .

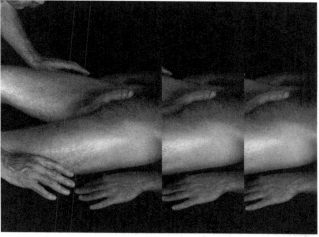

. . . down the arms and off the fingertips.

[Continued next page]

Then feather stroke from the top of the head . . .

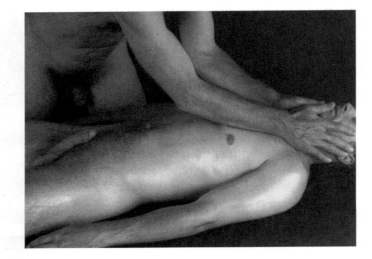

. . . down the torso, legs, and off the toes.

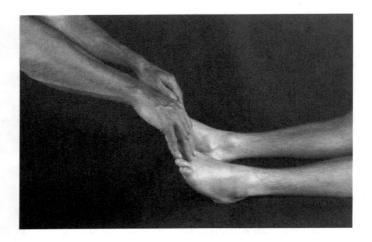

Now rest your hands on the feet with your thumbs
on the arches and your fingers on top of the
feet.
Again softly give breathing and imaging instructions: The inhalation comes up from the
bottom of the feet up to the top of the head.
The exhalation flows from the top of the head
down to the bottom of the feet.
After a couple of minutes, gradually allow your
hands to ascend, up off your friend's feet.

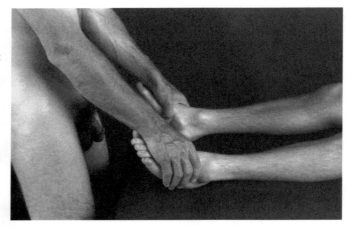

~ Often the genital massage stimulates sexual feelings and turns on the generator in the pelvic area. This
laying on of hands helps to awaken and expand the magnificent aliveness within us all.
Here you are dancing with the subtle energy flows of the Godbody. Your touch, your intending the flow of
energy, and your words all encourage you and your friend to become aware of our greater inner
beauty.

NECK AND HEAD

Your Position: Behind the head.

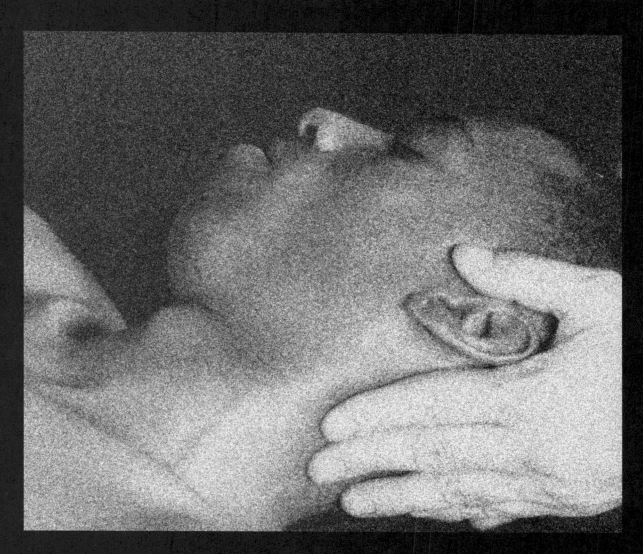

54 Connecting Stroke

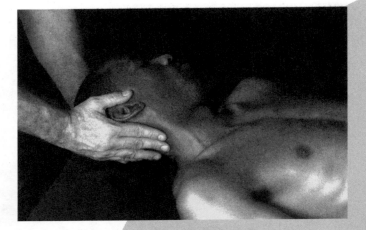

54·A

In preparation, hold your friend's head by placing
  your hand on the side of the head with your
  thumb in front of the ear and the fingers
  behind the ear.
Then rotate the head toward the opposite shoulder you will massage.
The image here illustrates how you place your
  right hand on the right side of his head before
  rotating the head to his right shoulder.

54·B

Place your left palm on the left shoulder and
  stretch downward.

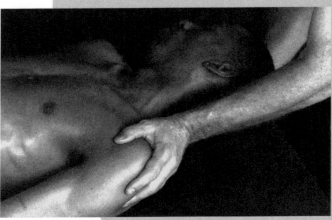

54·C

Discontinue the stretching and pivot your hand
  outward around the shoulder.

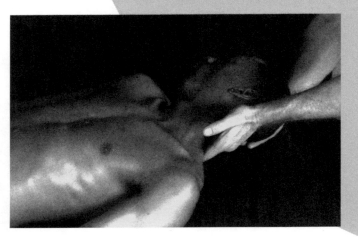

54·D

Firmly slide the flat of your fingers upward on the
  back of the neck (not on the throat) up to
  the base of the skull.

~ Repeat steps B, C, and D several times and then
  follow the same sequence on the other side
  of the neck, reversing the instructions for
  your right and left hands.

55 Let the Fingers Do the Walking

A and B

With the head resting on the heels of your
    palms, "walk" the finger pads upward on
    the back of the neck.
The "walking" is a sliding movement of alternat-
    ing fingers from the base of the neck
    toward the bottom of the skull.
Use a firm pressure with your fingers, but be
    careful not to pull the hair.

55·A

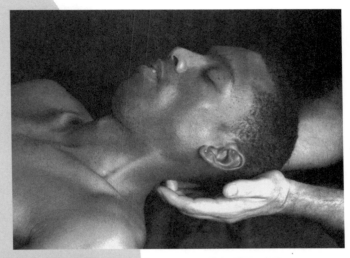

55·B

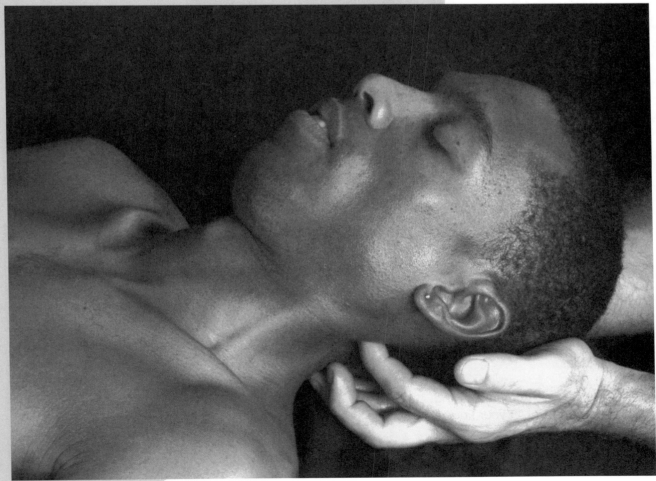

56 Head Scratch

56•A

Slide your finger pads back and forth
across the scalp on the underneath side of the head.

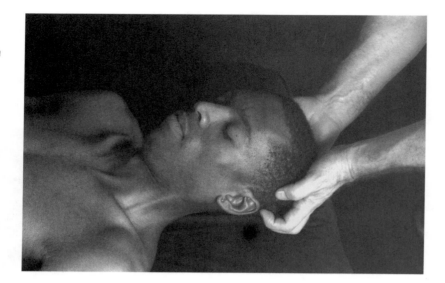

56•B

Move to your friend's right side and
turn his face to his right. Slide
your finger pads back and forth
across the scalp on the left side of
the head.
(Not illustrated here: If it's convenient,
move to his left side and turn his
face to his left so you can slide
your finger pads back and forth
across the scalp on the right side
of his head. Then move back to
your friend's right side to follow in
the manner as presented in the
following images.)

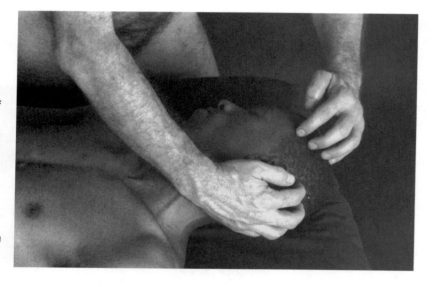

56•C

From his right side with his face
turned upward, slide your finger
pads back and forth across the
scalp on the sides and top of
your friend's head. Gradually
quicken the speed (but not the
pressure).

Not illustrated here: Without slowing
down, suddenly lift your fingers
off his head.

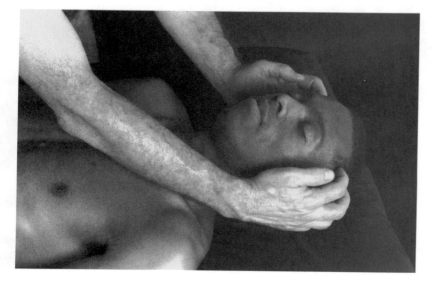

Wait a few moments, and then if possible, give a single light feather stroke with your fingertips from the head . . .

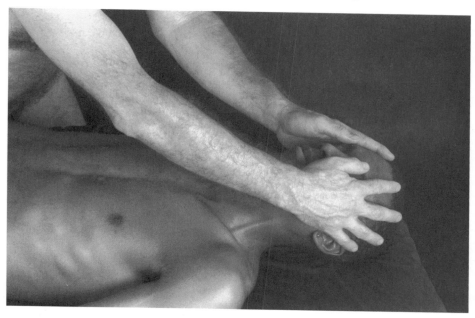

56•E   . . . down the chest, pelvis, thighs, and off the toes — all in one gentle sweep.

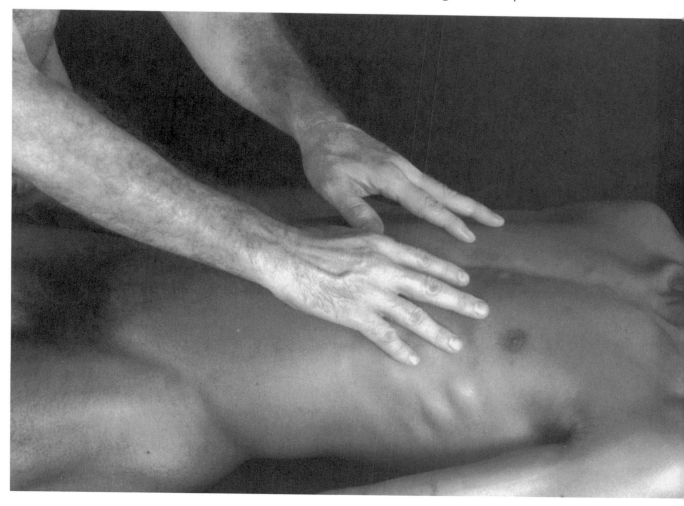

FACE

Your Position: Behind the head.

Note: For a facial massage, applying more oil would be excessive. However, if you have been using an unscented oil, you might try adding a small drop of scented oil to your hands to enhance the olfactory experience.

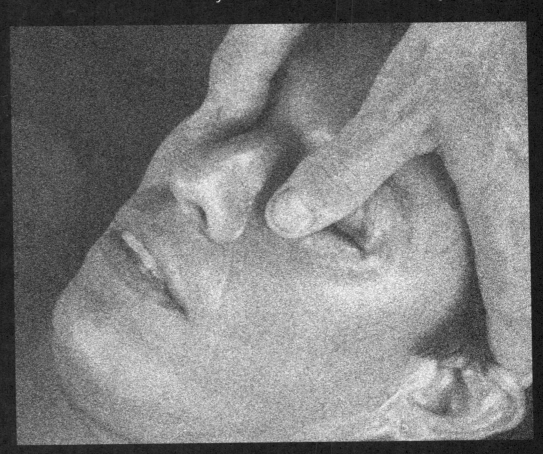

57 T Stroke

57•A

On the brow, slide your thumbs up . . .

B and C

. . . and across the brow.

~ Three or four repetitions will probably
cover the whole brow.

57•B

57•C

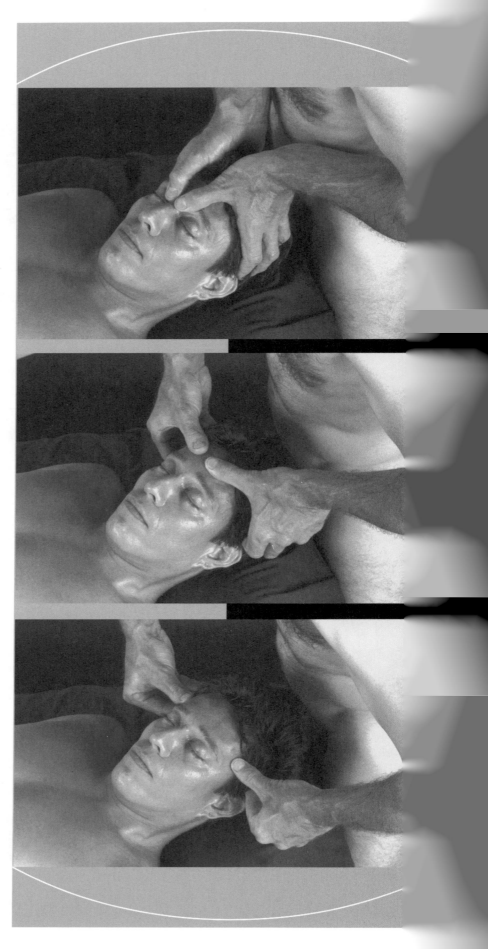

58 Eyebrow Squeeze

A and B

Make a series of squeezes of the eyebrows from the midline outward.

58•A

58•B

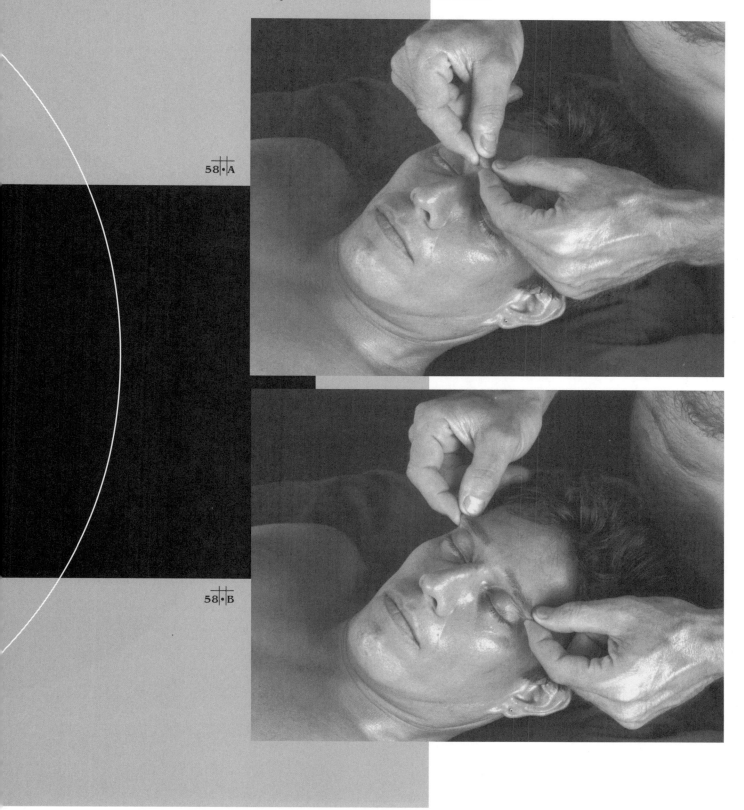

59 Temple Circles

A and B

Make several circle movements on the temples with flat fingers.

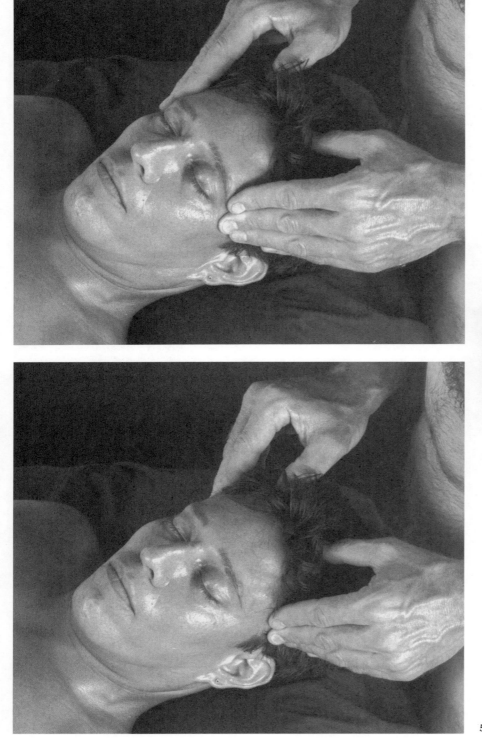

59•A

59•B

60 Underneath-the-Eyes Stroke

A and B

Slide your thumbs outward across the bony surface underneath the eyes, close to the
rim of the eye socket.

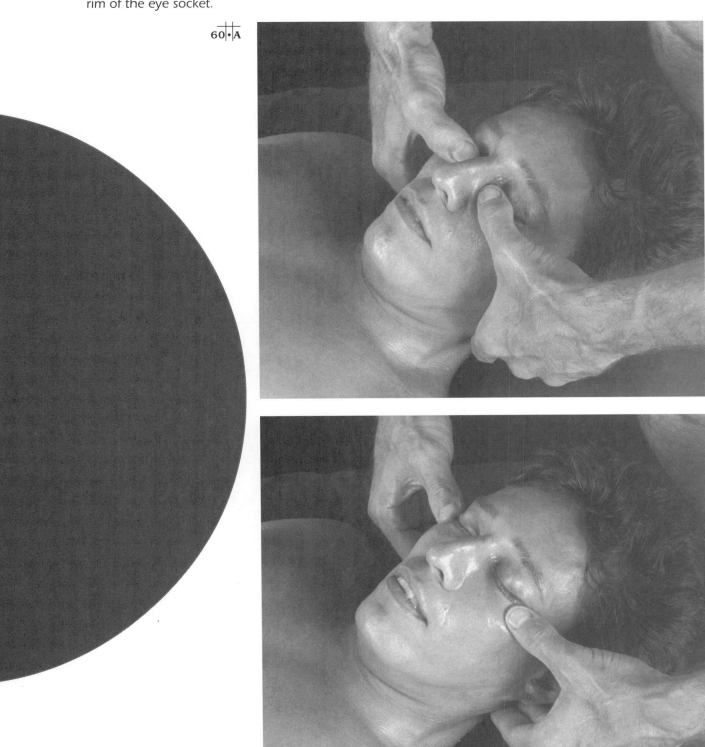

61 Eye Stroke

A and B

Massage the eyes only if hard contact lenses have been removed. Light pressure on soft lenses possibly may be OK. If uncertain, ask your friend.

Bracing the heel of your thumbs on the forehead, gently and slowly slide your thumb pads outward across the closed eyes.

~ Repeat two or three times.

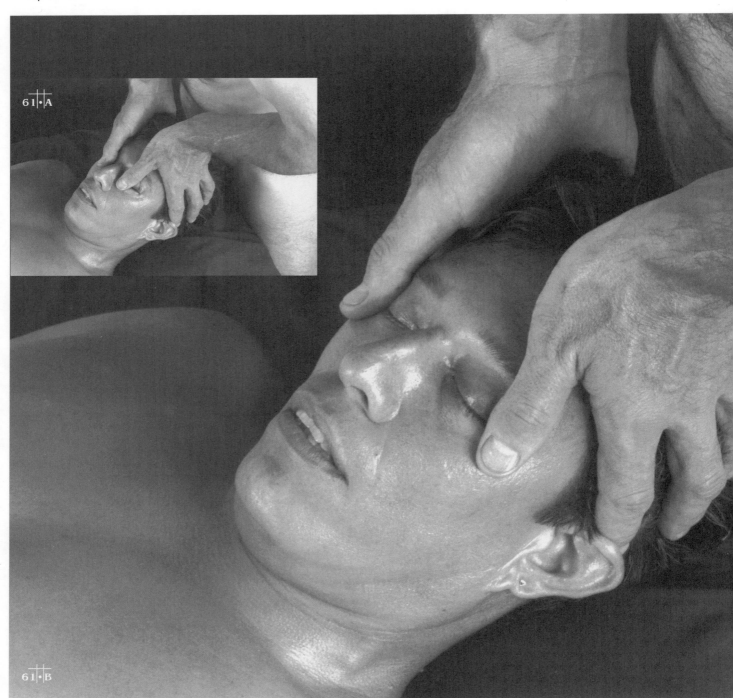

62   **Cheekbone Stroke**

A and B

Slide your thumbs outward across the top of
    the cheekbone.

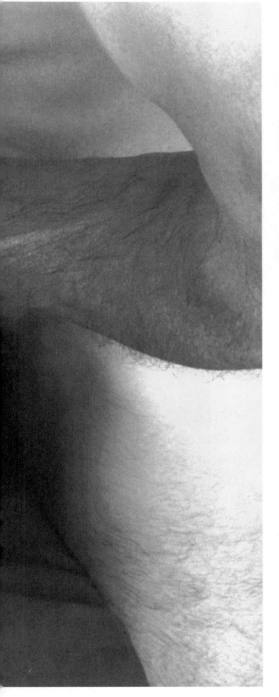

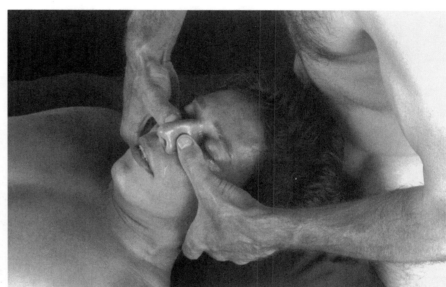

62•A

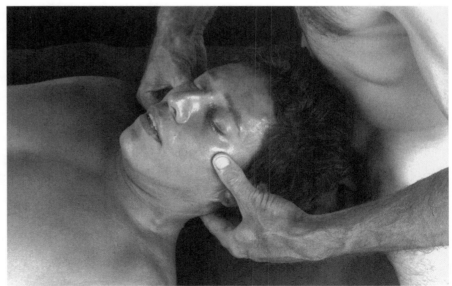

62•B

63 Under-the-Cheekbone Stroke

A and B

Slide your thumbs outward underneath the cheekbone.

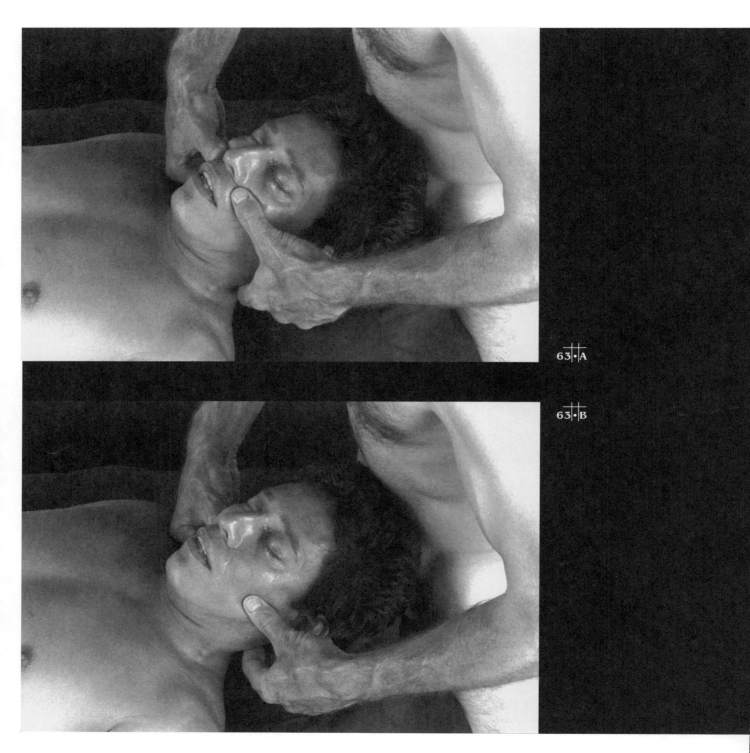

63•A

63•B

64 Jaw Circles

A and B

Make circle movements on the jaw area with the flat part of your fingers. Apply enough pressure so his skin slides over the muscles and bones beneath.

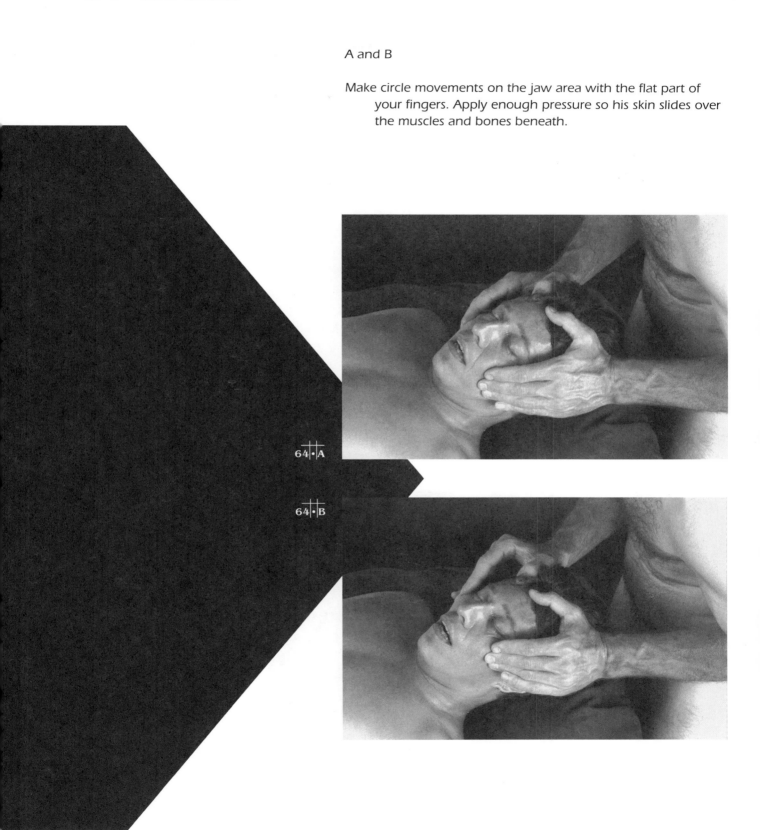

64•A

64•B

65 Upper Lip Stroke

A and B

Slide your thumbs outward across the upper lip.

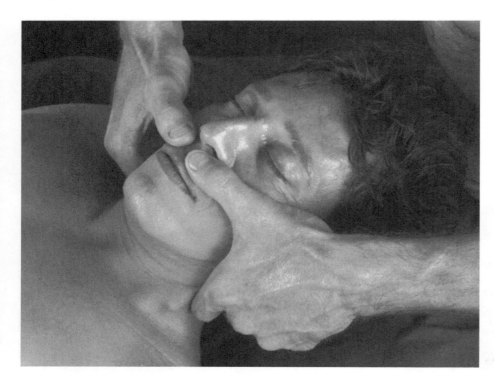

65 • A

65 • B

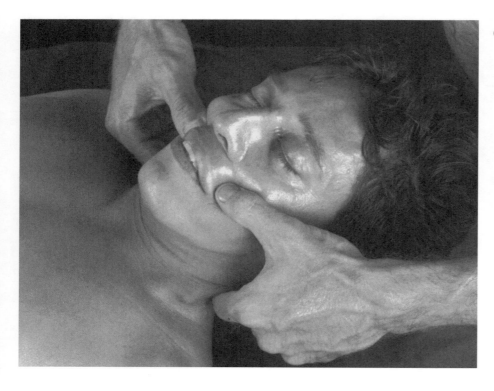

66 Lower Lip Stroke

A and B

Slide your thumbs outward across the
lower lip.

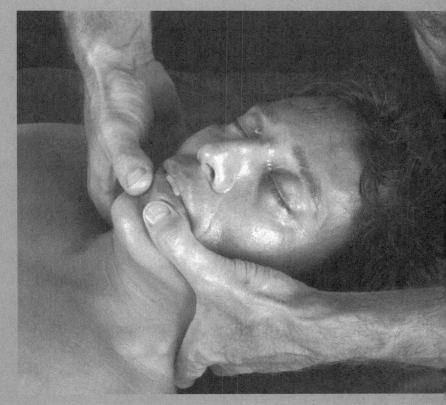

66·A

66·B

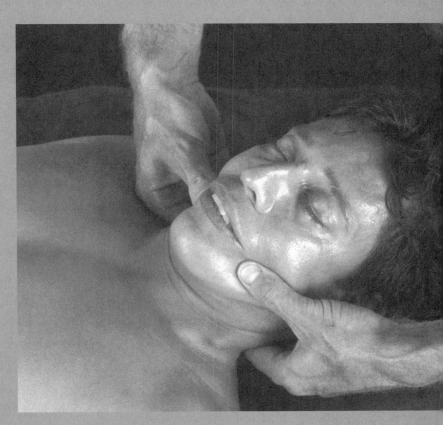

67 Throat Stroke

A and B

Gently slide your thumbs upward along the groove between the larynx and the sides of the throat.

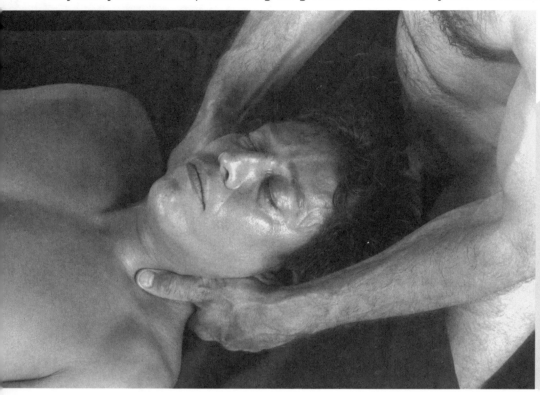

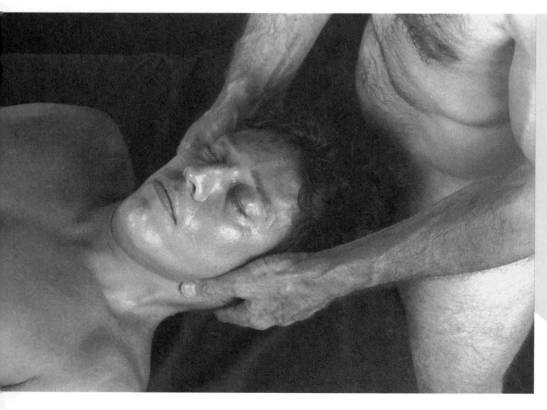

68 Behind-the-Ear Stroke

A and B

Slide your middle fingers up and down along the grooves behind the ears.

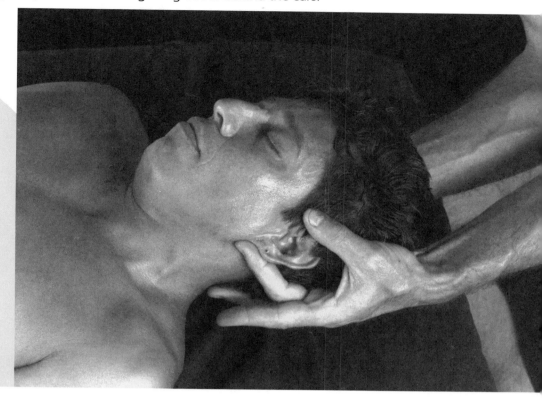

68•A

68•B

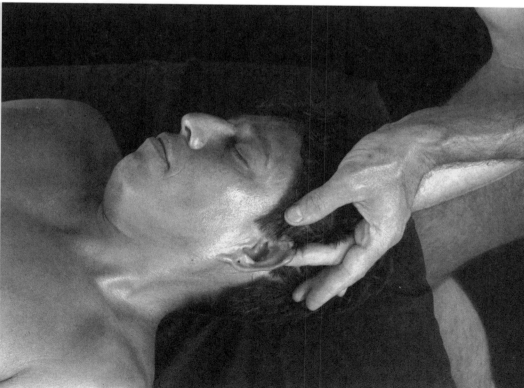

69 Outer Ear Stroke

69•A

With the pads of your thumbs and index fingers,
    gently squeeze the earlobes and slide
    outward to the edges of the ears.
(For illustration purposes, the demonstration is
    on only one ear in this image. Be certain to
    massage both ears at the same time.)

~ Repeat this as a series along the entire outer
    ear surface.

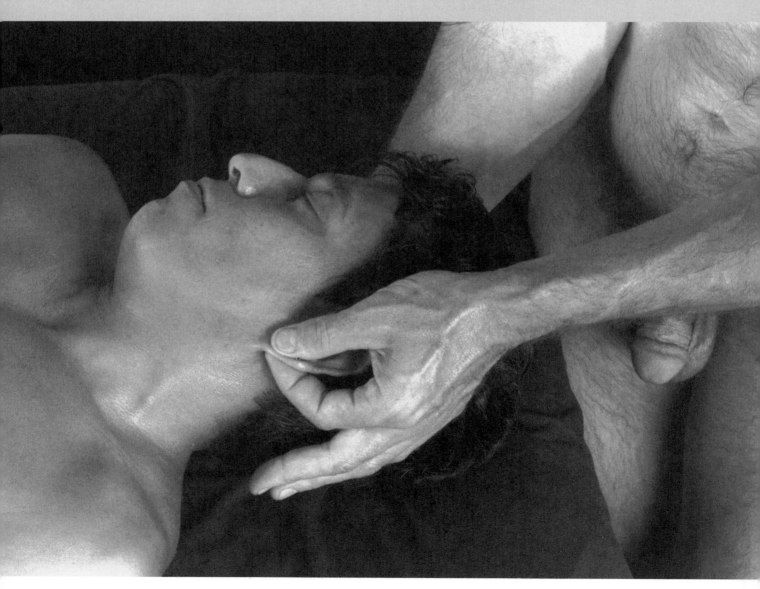

70 Inner Peace

70•A

Slowly slide your fingers into the ear canals and relax in this position for about a minute, blocking out the external sounds.

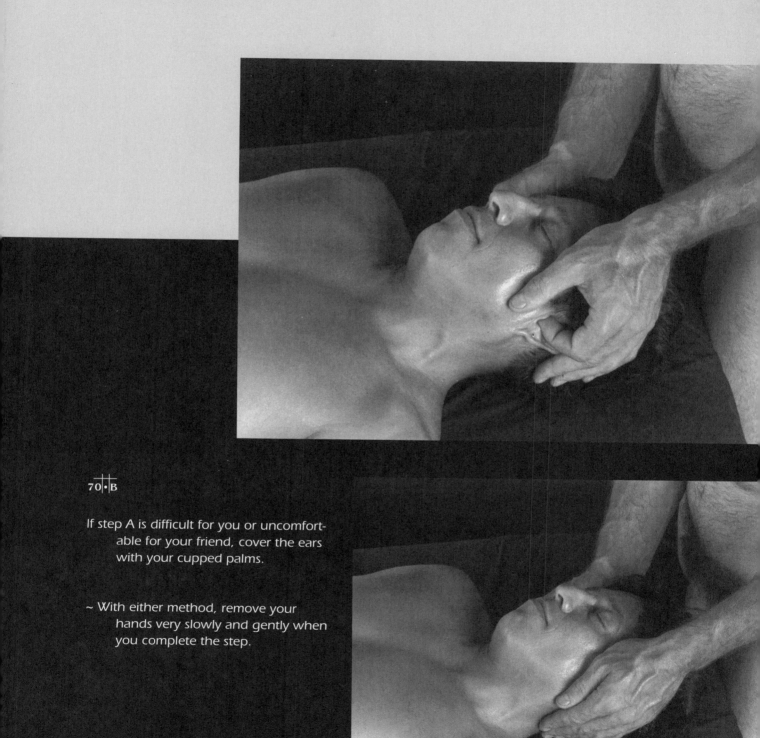

70•B

If step A is difficult for you or uncomfortable for your friend, cover the ears with your cupped palms.

~ With either method, remove your hands very slowly and gently when you complete the step.

MASSAGE
CONCLUSION

71 Concluding Stroke

 71·A

With your fingertips, lightly feather stroke from the top of the head . . .

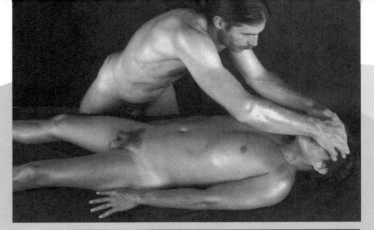

 71·B

. . . down off the fingertips.

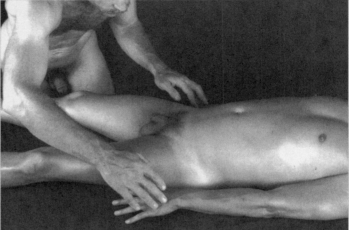

71·C

Then lightly feather stroke from the top of the head . . .

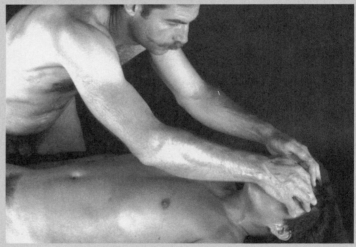

71·D

. . . down off the toes.

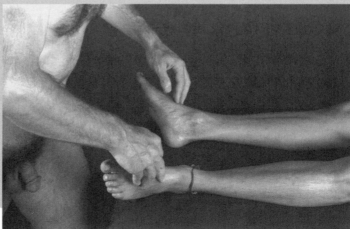

72 Covering

72·A

Unless it is very warm, cover your friend with a
    towel or sheet.

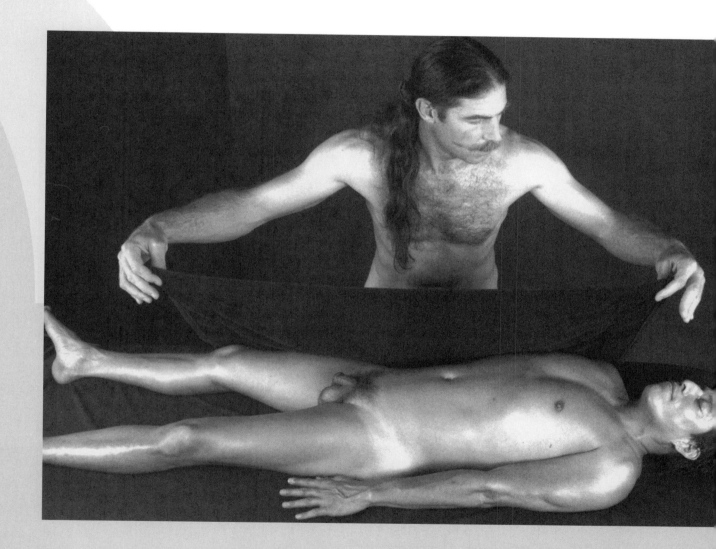

73 Laying on of Hands

73 • A

Rest your hands on the feet with your fingers on the top of the foot and the thumbs on the arches.
After a minute or so, very slowly allow your hands to ascend off.

~ Feel your own inner peace.

~ Remain silent until your friend returns to this world.

~ Embrace, if you wish.

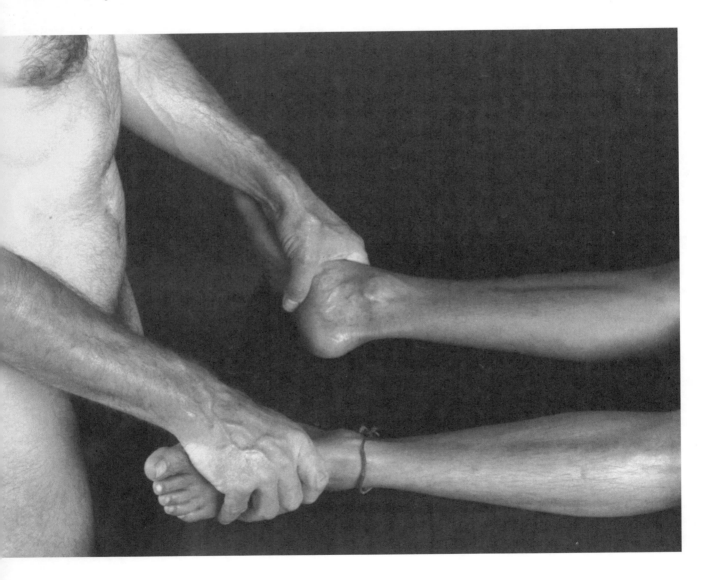

Additional Techniques

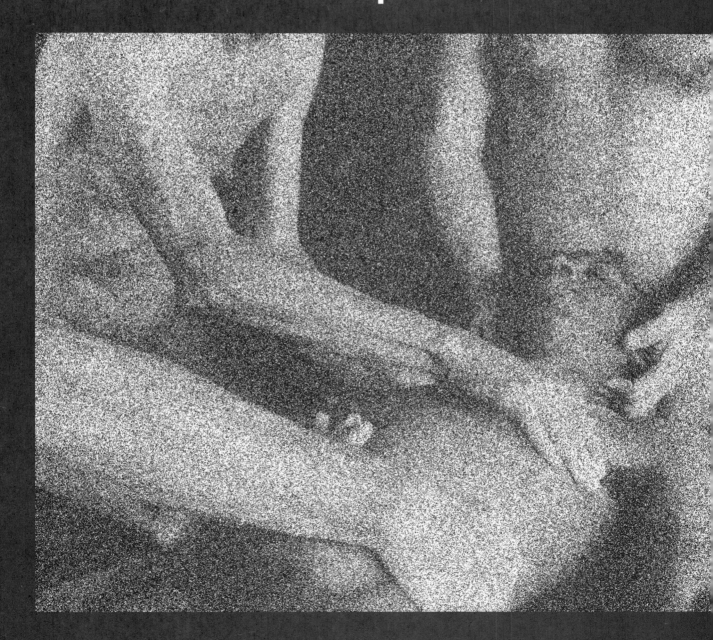

74 Feathers

74|•|A

If you wish, before you apply any oil,
   treat your friend to any of several
   delights.
Feathers, especially from peacocks or
   ostriches, can grace the surface
   nerve endings with exquisite
   titillations.
Let very long strokes remind your friend
   of the wholeness of his body.

75 Hair

75|•|A

Your own hair can give a very sensual nurturing. Explore the possibilities.

76 Furry Mitts

Also before you apply any oil, try
  stroking your friend with
  natural or synthetic fur or
  fabric.
Flowing, elongated movements are
  particularly nice. Vary the
  stroking patterns as they
  spontaneously appear. Have
  fun.

77 Safer-Sex Accessories

Should the giver or receiver prefer or need additional safer-sex
  precautions when massaging with just hands, vinyl or latex
  gloves from a pharmacy should provide excellent protection.
If the giver's hands have extremely rough skin, such as from long
  hours of manual work, the gloves can prevent many an unde-
  sirable snag.
Vinyl or latex gloves can also provide a nice sensation variation.

Note: Latex might cause some uncomfortable hair pulls on a hairy
  partner. So use more oil or try vinyl.

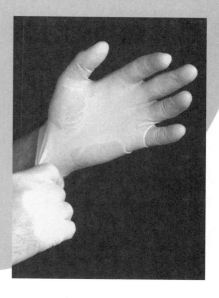

78·A

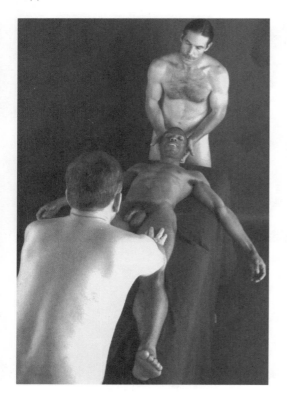

78·B

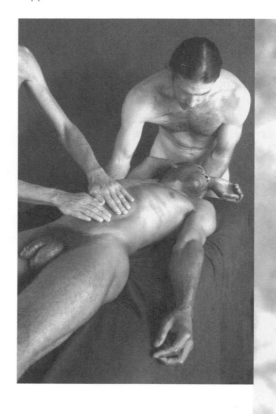

A through C

Often friends get together and
  share massage and companionship. Usually, sensitive
  touch is more important than
  an extensive repertoire of
  techniques.

Perhaps set an amount of time
  each person is to receive.
  Maybe permit the receiver to
  have some time to mellow
  immediately after his turn.

Food before, in the middle, or
  afterward can make the
  afternoon or evening of
  singing the body electric
  an occasion of nurturing
  camaraderie.

78·C

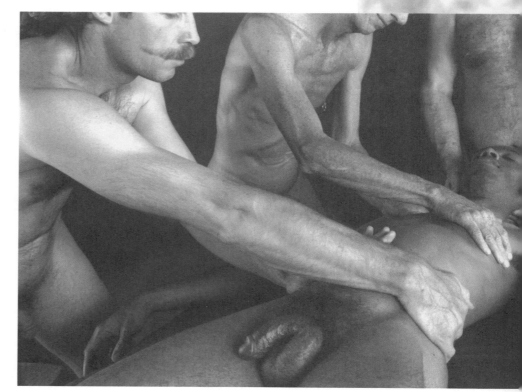

79•A

A and B

On the beach, in a meadow, on a porch, even high on a city rooftop, a massage can soar in ways not available inside.

Several precautions: too much sun, too cool, insects, noise, interruptions from unappreciative visitors. If necessary, give a mini-massage with clothes on, as in a public park.

79•B

DANCE OF THE GODBODY

Jim Dennis

In the images that follow, Jim Dennis reveals the Godbody's expression through various forms of human touch and contact.

The strength, the joy, the gentleness, the ardency, the tenderness, the pleasure, the play, the equanimity—these are all movements of the dance.

Allow these images to inspire your massage.

Allow the conscious energy of the Godbody to flow naturally through your being, bringing a presence and an honoring to your touch of another.

K.R.S.

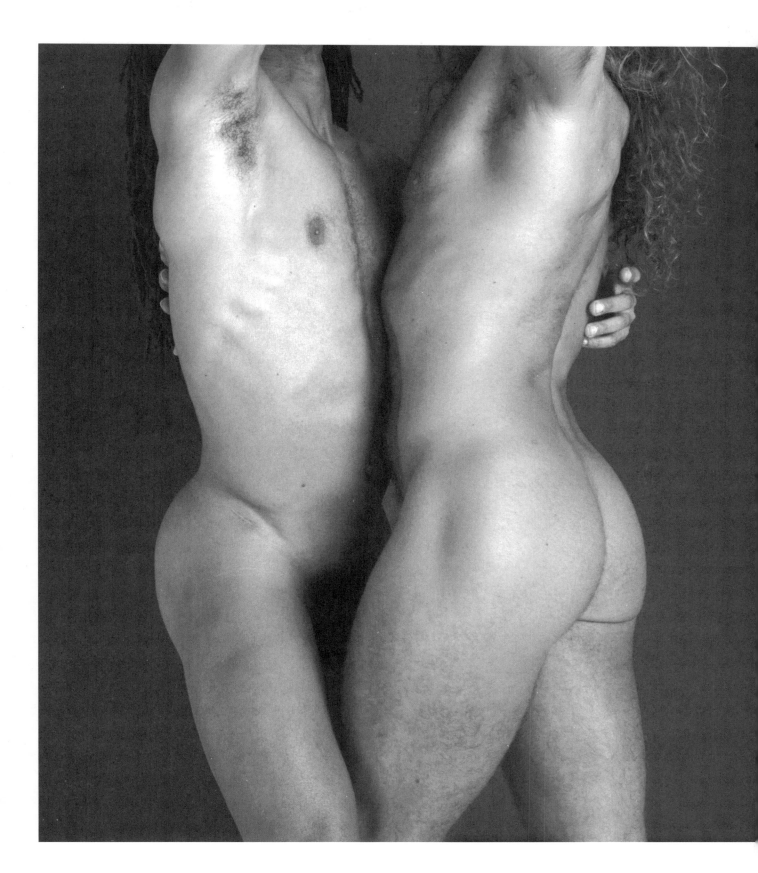

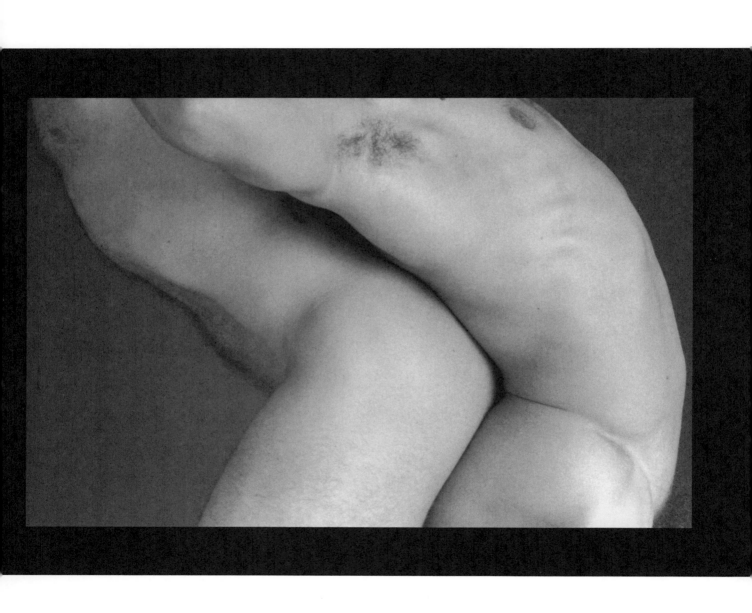

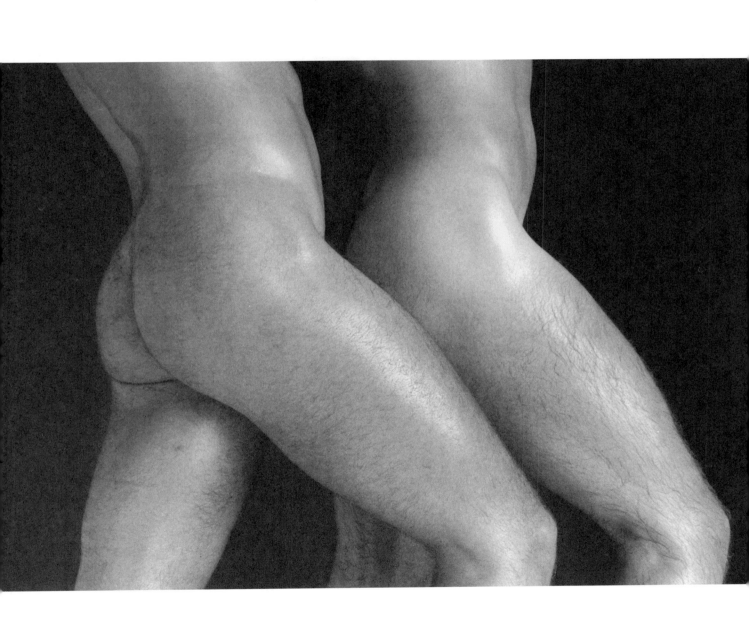

The Godbody

Kenneth Ray
Stubbs, Ph.D.

The poet, often far more than the priest, brings us to the sacred. Unbounded by dogma, a poet can sing the mystical hymn in celebration of it all.

Male Erotic Massage began with a psalm of praise to our essence: our spirit—dancing in the light. James Broughton's *Song of the Godbody* reveals a truth that can bring us to a view of massage outside the paradigms of everyday social convention, of science, and of many of our predominant religions, which would seldom consider two nude men sharing genital touch and pleasure as a spirit(ual) connection.

The truth revealed in James's *Song* is that we are more than a physical body.

He sings of our life force with such eloquence and joy that I borrow his term *Godbody* to refer to the subtle energies that bring life to matter.

The perspectives that follow are mine. They are esoteric, though from no specific tradition or belief system, and do not necessarily represent the views of James or any other participant in this book. I simply ask you to reflect on the words and adapt whatever may be useful for you—for in massage, we go by the body, not by the book.

First, God is neither male nor female. She is definitely not a gray-haired, bearded old man sitting on a throne in the sky. My personal term of choice at this time for this conscious energy is *Source*, sometimes *Great Spirit* or *Wakan Tanka*, sometimes *God/dess* or *Goddess*. I can honor all these titles. Out of general cultural convention, here we will use *God*.

Our soul, which is a part of God, likewise is neither gender. At some time after the sperm and the egg form a physical organism, our soul merges with this organism. In their dance together, the soul develops the Godbody, which is patterns of subtle energies we might call life or spirit and its myriad of expressions. Other spiritual traditions such as Tantra and Taoism might say *chakra*, *kundalini*, and *light body*, referring to different systems of the Godbody.

In a massage we are far more than hands sliding over skin and contour of another. Our Godbodies are connecting and responding as well. These subtle energies are actually as much a part of the massage as the physical body contact. The subtle flows and mergings of the Godbodies are what bring the emotional awakenings and spiritual profundity to which so many refer after receiving a massage.

The massage style presented in this book is sensual and meditative, emphasizing grace, flow, connection, and tenderness rather than fixing aches and curing illness. All styles of massage can benefit us. For learning the basics of massage, however, I have found the awareness of one's touch to be the most essential element in giving any style of massage. And this element is the focus of the *Male Erotic Massage* techniques.

The first one, "Centering," teaches "Be still, and know that I am God." [Psalms 46:10] Before you give the first touch, *be here now* with your self. Open your awareness to your wholeness, which is the physical body and the Godbody.

As you quiet your mind, emotions, and body in Centering, allow your Godbody to expand and come into harmony with the recipient. Like the Eastern mystic greeting another by folding his or her hands into the prayer position in front of the heart, bending slightly forward, and saying, "Namaste," let your inner prayer be the same in our language: "The sacred in me honors the sacred in you." This is the essence of the awareness we can bring to our touch of another.

When we are aware of our touch of another, we are present. When we honor another in intent and deed through our touch, we find our heart opening and feeling appreciation of our companionship, spiritual love, romance, sexual passion, or perhaps all of these.

As the dance of the massage unfolds, if the mutual presence and mutual appreciation deepen, someone able to see subtle energies might say the two Godbodies are merging into the same space. Or as expressed biblically, "For where two or three are gathered together in my name, there am I in the midst of them." [Matthew 18:20] This merging of subtle energies of the Godbodies and God, I call *at-one-ment*.

The key to at-one-ment is the willingness to allow each moment to unfold into the next, without attachment to the previous event and without expectation for the next event.

In most Western religious doctrines, the erotic would never be allowed as one of the unfoldments. In contrast, the middle word of this book's title is *erotic*. *A Guide to Sex and Spirit* is the subtitle. The text and the techniques and the photographs embrace both the spiritual and the sexual, for unless we allow all parts of the body and all human feelings to be among the consensual possibilities, we limit the unfoldment into at-one-ment. Likewise, forcing the erotic upon one's self or another in massage or in life equally restricts the possibilities of at-one-ment.

For the Godbody, the sexual and the spiritual are far from opposites. They are the center and the circle breathing in and out, integral dynamics of the whole. Actually, for the Godbody, there is no delineation between what our culture and minds label as sexual and as spiritual. Ultimately, it is all energy, and energy is neither good nor evil, only how we choose to dance with it.

For those who wish, embracing such a concept of our inherently sexual-spiritual nature can bring us to the freedom to delight in the *Song of the Godbody*'s evocation:

> *Let your feet itch with my glory*
>
> *Dance all the way to your death*

Appendix

Two Personal Stories

The following personal stories are from two people who were a part of the weekend photographic shoot for the massage techniques.

For the ending, we all sat in a circle and verbally shared the impact of being together intimately and intensely for several days, all focusing on the vision of men expressing nurturing touch with other men.

Far from being a collection of models assembled to photograph techniques, we had become a gathering of kindred souls. Listening to each in the circle, I realized we were communicating about the concerns and questions many have when they first begin to give and receive massage.

Afterward, I asked Delbert and Danielle to write down some of their experiences. Their insights can be lessons for us all.

As we read their stories, we can let their voices be a mirror of our humanity, our fears, and our strengths.

K.R.S.

To Come or Not to Come

Delbert Pentz-Newsome

My heart leapt with joy! That was my immediate response when told by a friend that Ray was putting together a new book for and about men, and that I should give him a call.

Then the little voices started in my head, "You can't do this! Everyone will know! How can you do this to your family?"

On and on they droned, and this was before I had talked to Ray and was thinking it was to be a book similar to his *Women of the Light: The New Sacred Prostitute*, i.e., written word only.

However, I could not forget that first leap of joy my heart had made. So, after three weeks of listening to every reason why I should not do this, I called Ray to say I was interested in appearing in his new book.

No! What have I done! He doesn't want my story! He doesn't want words! He wants my nude body displayed on page after page for the entire world to see!

Now you may wonder why someone with gold rings in his ears and nipples and with two tattoos in intimate places would care about being displayed nude at all? So did I! Why did this upset me so?

Here I am a 54-year-old man, born and raised a Southern Baptist in a small rural Kentucky town. I had attended a Baptist College before fleeing to New York and the theatre. My life as an actor and a pansexual seemingly didn't speak of prudery or subtlety. And years of living in cities such as Vienna, Amsterdam, Berlin, and Los Angeles, while studying many of the world's spiritual paths, had stripped all differences from the human race, leaving a mysterious spark of life as the one thing we all have in common. And that single spark can be fanned into flame through the ecstasy of sex.

The sexual act is the most spiritual act I know. And my rings and tattoos have a deep spiritual significance for me, one that is kept very private. To expose my body in a book was to demean that which I consider sacred. Or, so I thought.

It had taken me years of struggling with fear, shame, and blame to discover the sacredness of sex and the holy temple that is our body. Why would I want to hide that which I held most sacred? Why did I let the opinion of others keep me from sharing the good news?

My body is the holy temple for the life force that I am. It is through the senses that I can activate the life force and make the body truly electric. And, it is through touch that I am able to reach out to another holy temple and unite with their life force until we merge into something that is more than either of us alone.

With this understanding, I took my joyful heart to Tucson for a long weekend where men of other races and sexual preferences and I bared it all for the camera, for Ray, but ultimately for you, our brothers.

We had a wonderful, fun-filled time of putting words on hold so that we could focus on the universal language, the language of touch.

May this book help you discover and explore this language, one that needs no translation and which cannot be misunderstood, for it is a language which comes from the heart.

So, brothers, touch someone with your heart!

Touch someone with your hands!

Touch someone!

Let him touch you!

A View from a Woman

Danielle Berrien

I was two days away from spending one whole Saturday and Sunday in the company of men. Ray had invited me, several months prior, to be an assistant to him for the photographic shoot for his new book. I quickly and wholeheartedly had said yes. Suddenly, two days prior to the event I became really nervous. How would I be there as a female presence in the midst of this group of ten or so men? After considering fading into the background behind the veneer of "busy organizer-assistant person," I decided instead to try simply being myself.

Saturday morning Ray, Jim (the photographer), and I arrived at the site, excited and ready to go. Over the next few minutes to an hour, the men began to arrive and introductions were made. As each person entered the space, the simple ritual of smudging was performed. The sweet smell of the burning sage was a reminder to all, a calling, to hold clear our intentions for the photo shoot and our participation in the creation of this book. There was a palpable sense of excitement, some nervousness, and a feeling of anticipation.

Within a relatively short time the men had mostly begun to relax, some sharing conversations and shoulder rubs, becoming more open and intimate. It became quite apparent to me that I was witness to no ordinary group of men. Eventually, street clothes were exchanged for robes, wraps, and birthday suits.

With relaxing music playing in the background, Ray soon gave the cue for Joseph and Jacob to enter the set for the first round of photographs. They brought out the massage oil and took their positions. Ray and I settled in next to Jim, just in front of an incredible wall of luscious plants Allan and Susan have in their Tucson Creative Living Center, where we were doing the photographs. I took out the clipboard to track the shots taken on each roll, and Ray gave the directions for the first shot. Jim checked the lighting one more time and "click" went the camera. It had begun.

In an adjoining area where refreshments, Mexican food, salads, and more yummies were available, there was easy conversation flowing, shared stories and jokes. I remember a lot of laughter during the whole weekend.

At the end of the morning session, all the men appeared on the set for the group photo. Some had not yet met each other, but after a few nervous giggles, the bonding began to deepen. Something very magical was taking place.

Next was lunch. Sitting around the table eating, the men began intensely discussing the challenges and joys of relating with their partners—female or male, the challenges to their personal growth, and the rewards of relating with integrity. That they would choose relating and partnering as the first topic after only a few hours of being together was impressive, to say the least. I finished preparing my lunch plate and went to sit elsewhere, walking away with a quiet smile on my face and renewed respect mingled with deep joy in my heart. It was one of very few times I've experienced men that open, honest, and raw. I saw that men could be vulnerable (as women), very intelligent *and* spiritual, and funny as hell!

That evening when I went home and reflected on the day, I began to laugh and cry at the same time. My heart was so full! Since Cliff, my partner and one of the men in the next day's shoot, was out until much later, in our shared journal I wrote to him of my experiences of the day, of the laughter, the hugs, the looks without words, of the healing that had taken place.

On Sunday morning, greetings were different. Long hugs were exchanged, and tears . . . tears of joy and gratefulness, of being cracked open and whole. Jacob and I shared how we had wept the evening before with the wonder and beauty of it all. Several of us simply held the other's gentle gaze with tenderness and awe.

Memories from the day continue to return to my awareness. I can still hear Joseph talking about the importance of breath in experiencing and circulating the energy within. And my, what fun was had with the fur mitt! Especially the memory remains of my feelings of joy and appreciation as I watched Cliff being nurtured and touched by other men and he nurturing and touching them.

What was it like for these men to hold each other, and in ways our society deems as inappropriate and morally wrong? There was an ease and a comfort all of the men shared this weekend about holding each other's hands, embracing often, resting in the other's arms or touching so gently in a multitude of ways. It was inspiring to see. It was truly magnificent and beautiful to behold. There was an ease in which they shared their personal stories and a depth in their listening that belied the stereotypical "men don't know how to get personal and deep—they're too competitive." How utterly refreshing to witness as untrue.

After the final click of the camera, we all gathered together for a closing ceremony circle, a blessed opportunity to share thoughts, feelings, insights, prayers, and congratulations for the participation of each person present. I was honored by the men as a sister who supports them, and I truly do. Now, as never before, I can have and do have more compassion and respect for men, my brothers on this planet. I can no longer look at or think about men in quite the same way I used to. I realized how courageous it was for each man to *be* there, shedding more than clothes to participate in the magic and mystery of such an intimate photographic session.

It was a pleasure experiencing this group of men being committed to showing others by example that men can be nurturing, loving, sexy, witty, and wise. I appreciated their openness about who they are: their emotional and spiritual sensitivity, their power and strength, courage and vulnerability, and above all their humanness. I appreciated their seeking and their knowing. I delighted in their wisdom and their humor.

That weekend, I saw a reflection of myself through this beautiful myriad of men of all sexual orientations, different ethnicities and races, and diverse personalities. This reflection came to me not from their outward appearances, but from gazing into and lightly touching their souls. I saw men as if I were viewing through a wider-angle lens. I saw and deeply cherished human beings. Before I'd mostly only seen men, "the opposite sex." What a joyous gift!

Highly Recommended
Reading and Viewing

Fire on the Mountain: An Intimate Guide to Male Genital Massage, a video by Joseph Kramer, 1992, EROSpirit Research Institute, Oakland, CA.

An excellent complement to *Male Erotic Massage*, Joseph Kramer's video presents possibly the greatest number of male genital massage strokes in any single source.

Fire on the Mountain begins with a breathing pattern and a series of meditative movements to be practiced with a partner. This is to awaken and enliven the physical body and Godbody.

Then, continuing with the breathing pattern, two men demonstrate a wide variety of genital strokes that will surely augment anyone's repertoire.

The breathing pattern is the key to what Joseph often terms Taoist erotic massage. Ancient Chinese Taoist sexual practices are renowned for their emphasis on delaying ejaculation for the male and intensifying pleasure. Following *Fire on the Mountain* can definitely intensify your and your partner's enjoyment. Highly recommended.

Erotic Massage: The Complete Edition, a video by Kenneth Ray Stubbs, Ph.D., 1989, Secret Garden Publishing, Tucson, AZ.

Flowing from the same philosophy of sex and spirit integration as *Male Erotic Massage*, this video demonstrates all the strokes in the book plus female genital strokes.

The *Erotic Massage* video shows the grace, the flow, the dance of erotic massage that cannot be conveyed in still photographs. A valuable adjunct to the *Male Erotic Massage* book.

Evolutionary Masturbation: An Intimate Guide to the Male Orgasm, a video by Joseph Kramer, 1996, EROSpirit Research Institute, Oakland, CA.

Only to the extent we can be erotic with ourself can we be an erotic lover with another. Joseph Kramer's video of self-massage on the male genitals is an extremely valuable preparation for learning to give erotic massage to another.

Massage is principally a tactile sensory art. As we place the bodily sensations at the center of our meditative and massage focus, we deepen our ability to experience the integration of our physical body and Godbody. Worlds of subtle energies abound within us. Intensifying and expanding these energies is more easily accomplished through our sexuality than probably any other aspect of our humanity.

Joseph's video presents many practical keys to open doors to discovering how to touch, massage, awaken, and enlighten our sensory/sexual/spiritual self. An excellent visual workbook.

Anal Pleasure and Health: *A Guide for Men and Women*, revised third edition, a book by Jack Morin, Ph.D., 1998, Down There Press, San Francisco, CA.

When the first edition of *Anal Pleasure and Health* appeared in 1981, it immediately went to my eminent books' shelf beside other sexological authors such as Kinsey, Masters and Johnson, Havelock Ellis, and Bronislaw Malinowski.

Now in its third edition, Jack Morin's breakthrough *Anal Pleasure and Health* is a major contribution of information and reason on what some would call no-man's land. With compassion and wisdom, Jack confronts one of modern society's most irrational taboos.

Male Erotic Massage does not demonstrate anal massage because I felt that bookstores are not yet ready to present vivid photographic representations of such a charged topic. Moreover, both Jack and I are quite familiar with the sometimes subtle, sometimes blatant, self-imposed, sexually repressive censorship in the mainstream publishing, printing, and binding industries, something not obvious to the general public.

I strongly encourage you to read Jack's book, and if you desire, to adapt the information to complete the otherwise full-body massage presented in *Male Erotic Massage*.

Erotic Celebrations: *The Films of James Broughton, Vol. 1*, a video collection of films by James Broughton, 1992, Facets Video, Chicago, IL.

Rather than teaching massage and touch techniques as the preceding suggestions do, this collection of four avant-garde films reveals the erotic art of the body, of touch and play, of the dance of the Godbody. Here James Broughton reads his poem *Song of the Godbody* as the background to his film of the same name. And *Hermes Bird* . . . well, I considerate it the most erotic short film of the twentieth century.

Acknowledgments

First, I wish to thank the many friends and lovers who over the years agreed to play show-and-tell with me so I might learn what massage school would not teach. And to the many people throughout North America and Europe who entrusted your bodies, minds, and spirits into my hands while organizing or attending my various hands-on seminars, you brought me much knowledge and wisdom about sex and spirit. This and my other books would never have been created without you.

Male Erotic Massage is also very much the expression of Jim Dennis, the photographer. Jim is an exploring, mellow soul who has made this project so much more of a joy to create. His enthusiasm is like a child's at play in a visual wonderland.

Richard Stodart designed much of this book's look and feel. His artistic wisdom enabled me to focus on what I knew best while leaving the challenge of breathing life into the presentation of the text and technique photos to him. My life is deeply enriched by his companionship.

James Broughton, the poet of the *Song of the Godbody*, is going to heaven when he leaves—'cause that's where he's from. Each time he incarnates in a newborn body, the elves dance around his crib day and night, and tickle him, and invoke him to sing his wild merriment to the world. This sage has blessed us all this lifetime. Thus, this book is dedicated to him.

And I greatly appreciate Joel Singer, James's partner, who has made all the arrangements easy. James and Joel were among the first to attend my erotic massage for men seminars in San Francisco. Since then, they have gifted me with their creative beauty and graced my consciousness on many occasions.

Jack Morin and Joseph Kramer wrote the Foreword and Introduction, respectively. I am honored they are willing to be a part of this book. They are heroes for me, for each has had a moment of decision: to step outside the boundaries and become outlaws in a deeply sexually repressive culture, or to remain within the confines of convention and ignorance. Because of their pioneering choices and determination, we all have more knowledge. We have more freedom.

In alphabetical order of their first name, these are the brave souls who came together in ceremony one spring weekend to bare their all for Jim Dennis's camera in the Tucson desert: Cliff Berrien, Delbert Pentz-Newsome, Jacob Palafox, John E. Kent III, Joseph Kramer, Tim Dingman, and Tim

Townsend-Kuhns. We all had a memorable connection that weekend. My memory of the warmth and caring expressed among these men of all sexual orientations and varied racial and ethnic backgrounds has often inspired me while bringing together *Male Erotic Massage*.

Others behind the scenes made that photographic weekend flow amazingly. Danielle Berrien's ability to remain grounded and on purpose while assisting during the many stresses of the shoot made all our lives easier. Allan Sorokin, Susan Swan, and their newly presented dream, the Tucson Creative Living Center, gifted our eyes with a panoramic view of hundreds of saguaros in the Sonoran Desert, behind the backdrop cloths. They were incredibly supportive. Marc Haberman and Richard Poethig made many of the lodging and food arrangements a much-simplified detail. And Jeffrey A. Goodman was the angel who, on Saturday night when all local photographic supply sources were closed, came to our rescue with a neighborly loan of essential electrical equipment which literally had just gone up in a puff of smoke in the heat of our shoot.

Jim Dennis photographed the men in the "Dance of the Godbody" section over a two-year period in his studio. Our agreement was that the men's identity would be private. I wish to convey my appreciation to these men for their expressions of gentleness and strength, of tenderness and passion.

Nancy Carleton, fresh off the grind of managing a political campaign, shifted gears and served once again as trusty copyeditor, saving me from those embarrassing grammatical errors and typos that can somehow sneak into a first printing and live forever.

On the home-office front, Nancie Ennis handled so many of those interfering day-to-day details that prevent books from reaching the reader. She makes my life so much less stressful. Thank you!

Scott Burr's and Louis Jandrell's technical computer advice prevented many a headache. Their support was invaluable.

Patrick and Paul did not know it, but they were the catalyst that brought this book into "now it's time to do it."

In conclusion, I wish to honor the erotic masseurs and masseuses who touch others with compassion. You are the modern sacred prostitutes without a temple, usually without a wise mentor guiding you to the depths you can reach within another. *Male Erotic Massage* presents the massage techniques with only a hint of the awesome magnitude of the Godbody. Remember that when you dance with the sexual energy in massage, if you dance with sacred intent and compassion, you dance with God.